DOUWES FINE ART

SINCE 1805

200 YEARS

STADHOUDERSKADE 40

1071 ZD AMSTERDAM THE NETHERLANDS

TEL. +31 (0)20 - 664 63 62 FAX +31 (0)20 - 664 01 54

E-MAIL: info@douwesfineart.com INTERNET: www.douwesfineart.com

"It's easy to speak of 'timeless' when believing in the hereafter"

TABLE OF CONTENTS

ACKNOWLEDGEMENTS

For their invaluable advice and help in preparing this catalogue, we would like to thank the following people:

- our wonderful staff: Willemien, George, Manon, Gabriëlle, Marie-Françoise, tante Lies, Nadja, Paulien, Karin, Willem , Cynthia and Ronald. Through the years, they have given us much of their time and dedication in supporting our family business in every way possible.

- our enthusiastic colleagues, who have inspired us to realize a unique exhibition of Rembrandt prints: Eberhard Kornfeld, Christine Stauffer, C.G.Boerner and Armin Kunz, David Tunick, Kunsthandlung Rumbler, and several private collections.

- our various suppliers, without whose finishing touches it becomes ever more difficult to put our paintings, drawings, watercolours and etchings on offer. Particularly, the staff of framemakers at Paul Gehring's, the paper restorers at Elisabeth Nijhoff-Asser's, and the photo laboratory of S-Color.

- several journalists and publishers, who have done a great job compiling our family story from personal interviews and examining the archives. 'Tableau Magazine' in particular, with Annemieke van der Wilt, Anja Frenkel and Ronald Kraayeveld; 'More Than Classic', with Hugo Kosters, Erik Jager and photographer Freek Esser; 'Ons Amsterdam', with Marius van Melle; and many others.

- my former teacher Leen Don for his help in turning it all into 'readable' English, and who, together with his wife Irene, spent many hours tied to his computer, and was able to follow the tenor of our thoughts in the complexity of the information. His quick humour made it seem like 'a piece of cake'.

- our catalogue designer and photographer Kees Kuil, with whom we have established a unique and creative collaboration, literally working day and night in order to lend a very personal Douwes family touch to the present result. We thank him for his patience and his efforts in arranging the supply of high-quality paper, donated by M-real Zanders.

"The history of the heart is much more important, than the history of Ar

INTRODUCTION

The universal saying *'Nihil (fit) sine causa'* ('Nothing happens without reason') seems to be part and parcel of the many generations of our Douwes family business. It is aptly demonstrated by this 200-year anniversary.

Our forefathers worked hard in the process of serving our profession, and over time perhaps often almost forgot to mark their various jubilee occasions. It was not felt as their first priority. Yes, of course, we do visualize Henri celebrating 100 years of Douwes Fine Art in 1905, possibly in a modest way, with perhaps a few newspaper clippings mentioning what was even then a unique milestone. But what to think of a Jubilee of 200 years!? And how will society react to the uniqueness of it, because to be honest, is there a precedent to follow, in the world of art dealing? Worldwide there are, perhaps, only a few companies still existing that can boast of such a feat.

It is already some twenty-five years ago that I philosophised about the existence of our long-standing family tradition, and jotted down the following note: *"the value of tradition is knowing when to break with it"*. However, it is remarkable to observe that the majority of clients and professionals take the continuation of such a long-existing business for granted, even against all odds. Of course, we have weathered the storms of 200 years, including several devastating wars and economic crashes worldwide.

During the last thirty years, however, collecting art has become far more of an investment game. The scarcity of objects, international competition, the possibility for collectors to 'shop around' using the internet, bidding at auction houses and visiting art fairs, have all been reasons enough to chip away at the old-fashioned loyalty, which was so important to the functioning of the traditional art dealer. Rooted deep inside us are the passion and love for art, the constant attempt to renew our expertise, the willingness to render comprehensive services such as advice on buying and selling, the caring for objects that have been consigned to us, the restoration of paintings, the art historical research, the giving of lectures on various themes in art, the provision of valuations for insurance and inheritance.

This is the opportunity to thank all our family members, past and present, for their selfless efforts in continuing a unique family tradition of art dealing and restoring. For their shared passion for art, and the openness with which each generation have contributed to spreading the liberating appreciation of beautiful objects and thoughts. And additionally, to thank not only the active partners in our own business, but equally, all other family members that support us in keeping alive the continuity of this fine profession. In the context of this particular Jubilee exhibition, we are especially grateful for the support and loyalty of our dedicated group of clients, for their trust and confidence in our firm, for consigning to us their precious objects. In addition, we thank our colleagues for lending to us, and our partners for sharing with us, some of the art works on display. We equally want to express our appreciation to the art historians for their constant help in keeping us focussed on the essential knowledge of past and present.

And, as for myself, I want more than anything to praise my brothers Erick-Hans and Peter and my sister Pia, and most of all my amazing parents, my wonderful wife Jeanneke and our talented children, for their unremitting and undivided love and attention. They keep my batteries charged and my mission in life clearly focussed.

It is the deepest wish of all of us to continue our fine family tradition in a prudent and enjoyable manner, serving collectors and prospective buyers with the best knowledge available to us. Certainly, we shall do our utmost to preserve our traditional expertise and service in generations to come.

With best wishes and good hunting,

Evert Douwes VII and Evert Douwes VIII

Damrak 69, Amsterdam in 1912

Douwes Fine Art
since 1805

Europe's oldest single-family art gallery
celebrates its 200th Anniversary

t. Luke', Antwerp School, c. 1540

The Douwes tradition started with a restoration workshop as early as the 1760's, because already in the fashionable Amsterdam of the second half of the 18th century, the Douwes forebears tried to meet the desire of those that wanted the beautiful ceilings of their imposing canal houses painted and restored.

These days, the firm still belongs to the same family, and has been passed on from father to son for many generations. The present owners of Douwes Fine Art are in effect the seventh and eighth generation. However, according to the official regulations of the St.Lucas guild, abolished shortly after in 1808, they prefer to start counting from their entry as an independently registered business on September 5th, 1805. Now in its sixth generation of art dealing and restoring since then, this prestigious art gallery is the oldest of its kind in The Netherlands, and in Europe.

Whoever speaks to Evert Douwes Sr. and Jr. about two hundred years of Douwes Fine Art, is impressed by their passion for art and by their knowledge. Two ingredients that have been providing a rich and wide-ranging life for generations. Wide-ranging, because Douwes is so much more than painting. There is and was calligraphy, topography, writing about history, documenting, restoring, and…. the selling of works of art. But Europe's oldest family art gallery cannot be resting on its laurels. On the contrary, the art market of 2005 is complicated, and has been changing too much.

This did not worry **Hendrik Douwes**, when in 1805 he decided to officially register his own business. Hendrik was the son of a shipwright and restorer called Evert, and the third of seven children. He married Maria de Ruijter, and together they had two children. Of these two, the boy was once again called Evert.

The enterprising twenty-year old signed the 'burgher oath' ('poorter eed') allowing him to set himself up independently and join the artists guild St.Lucas. And an artist and craftsman he was at that time. He practiced crafts that ranged from the painting of theatre decors and boats to the gilding and bronzing of picture frames. The Amsterdam of 1805 was busy developing scientific knowledge and the resulting first tentative technologies.

5

Many societies began to emerge to exchange that knowledge and experience. They had ringing names such as "*Vlijt is de Voedster der Wetenschappen*" ("Diligence is the foster mother of the Sciences"). Best-known society was "*Felix Meritis*", which aimed at the promotion of the arts and the sciences. Hendrik must have spent many an interesting evening in the well-known building on the Keizersgracht, and will also certainly have made friends with future customers. The society became a beacon of the new times that were slowly evolving from the traditional into the industrial. Hendrik himself was still working in a purely traditional way, but was also in the meantime cautiously orientating himself towards the art of painting itself, and occasionally canvases of artist friends decorated his walls.

Evert IV and Hendrina Douwes-Sl

All his amassed knowledge was handed down to **his son Evert** (1809–1869), who followed the road taken by his father, but also expanded the firm. In 1835, he married the Roman Catholic Hendrina Sluyter, and together they had no less than nine children. The family lived over the workshop on the N.Z. Achterburgwal, the present Spuistraat. A frame-making department was added. From the old records, we can infer that a gilded gold leaf frame cost 80 guilders. At present, this would have amounted to 6000 Euros.

Evert V

Led by Evert's energetic sons, **Evert** (1843-1896) and **Henri** (1850-1938), it became business in earnest. Aged 26 and 19, they changed the company's name into "*Gebroeders Douwes*" ("Douwes Brothers"), consisting of an art gallery, a frame-making department, and a restoration workshop, all situated at the Grimburgwal nr.15, in Amsterdam. Henri became a genuine "Amsterdam expert", and expert in topographic maps of Amsterdam, prints, and contemporary art. He was married to Francisca M. Engelkamp, and together they had four daughters, and a son Evert Josephus Maria.

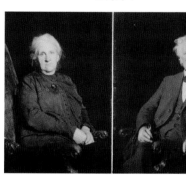

Francisca and Henri Douwes-Engel

The restoration workshop became an even more important part of the art gallery, and throughout those two centuries it remained a thread running through the firm's history. The well-known restorer and painter of landscapes W.J.Walter became Henri's tutor. Among other things, he taught him the art of relining. The present Evert Jr. (1953): "My great-grandfather had that drive to want to perfectly master the art of restoring. You can imagine that as a restorer you are also a bit of an artist. What was it the painter intended to convey, what techniques were used? You try to get under the artist's skin in order to preserve as much as possible of the authenticity of the piece." Henri's striking facial features betray his being more of an artist than a dealer. That the business survived at all, was because of his wife, for Henri – called "Paatje Douwes" ("Daddy Douwes") by the family – often gave customer friends an etching or other work to take home "and see how it looks". His wife saw to it that it would indeed be paid for.

...nt from our glass negative, c. 1900

...ards in traditional costumes, c. 1900

Cornelis Vreedenburgh

After 1880, photography started to play a significant role in the life of the Douwes brothers. Henri (brother Evert had died in 1896 at the age of 50) was a passionate photographer who, just as his contemporaries Jacob Olie and George Breitner, roamed the town in order to capture the images of Amsterdam. Modern times demanded alterations to be made in the town. Canals were filled, streets widened, and offices built. Photography made it possible to preserve the old and the new town views. The latter can be observed in the watercolour "Horses and the building of Houses" by Breitner, which even in 1923 fetched 1375 guilders. Collecting and trading photographic town views and glass plate negatives became an integral part of the firm.

The 1885 opening of the Central Station gave an impulse to tourism. (Right from the opening of the railway track, Henri had been commuting from Bussum to Amsterdam, and in 1935 was honoured by the Railways as their oldest customer). Henri Douwes responded to tourism by selling brownish picture postcards to the day-trippers for a tiny amount. Americans also started to visit the gallery and bought the entire supply of "Dam-views". Because of their move to the Damrak in about 1901/1902, where dealing in paintings was starting to become more and more dominant, 28 handcarts of prints were auctioned off. But his passion for Amsterdam prints had not cooled. At auctions, Henri was playfully called the "glutton".

Tourists could even have their pictures taken in traditional costumes. Evert Douwes Sr. (1928) now still remembers costumed dolls in the gallery window. His father and aunt had served as models for the camera, dressed in Volendam or Marken costumes. As a matter of fact, these fishing villages with their populations dressed in traditional costumes were an additional favourite tourist destination.

The Dutch town view was an important subject in the second half of the 19th century, the time of Romanticism. Painters such as Springer, Vertin, and Adrianus Eversen were wandering artists that have recorded and visualised many such a town view. They will undoubtedly have submitted their canvases and panels to Henri, which, after being taken there by handcart, will have graced the walls of the gallery. Henri either bought them or held them on consignment.

A prominent artist was Klinkenberg. His town views were very clear and lively. To try and sell Johannes's latest works, he did the rounds using his carrier cycle. At that time, 800 guilders would already have to be paid for his art. Douwes Sr.: "When in 1928 his studio was auctioned off, my father bought a 17th century four-door Dutch cabinet, which is now at my son's."

From 1905 onwards, the works of art that were traded, were photographed. That is how we know that Henri regularly acquired Amsterdam town views and South Holland landscapes from painters like Cornelis Vreedenburgh. Or from lesser-known masters such as Van Prooyen and Rijkelijkhuizen. They were bought by passing tourists or art-loving brokers working at the nearby Stock Exchange, who Henri met on his daily train runs. They became good customers.

Amsterdam and its history were Henri's passion. He made pictures, collected and traded old town maps, painted town views, and knew everyone that occupied himself in an artistic and historical manner with Amsterdam. In the meantime, his restoration workshop had moved to new premises in the Warmoesstraat nr. 73. The ornamentation business – many an Amsterdam signboard was made here – was sold off because of a diminished demand.

Henri Douwes and his restorers, c.

Douwes Sr.: "My grandfather's heart was with the Amsterdam etchings and prints. He had a vast collection and shared his passion with among others Willem Dreesmann, father of the recently deceased Anton Dreesmann. Willem had various collection fields, just as his father; but his preferences tended towards the Amsterdam town views. In the arts, the two families were closely linked for generations. Catholicism also played its part in this. To all these prints, Henri added descriptions. The lithograph became popular in about 1900, and caused a boom in prints. It was one of Henri's passions. At one time, I found an original engraving of the Nieuwmarkt (New Market) with the Waag (the Scales). Written on its back, I discovered an elaborate historical description in my grandfather's handwriting, dated 1923."

As Senior now says, "Douwes Brothers during **the first one hundred years was art with a small 'a'**. A small firm, from a good location in Amsterdam dealing on a limited scale in all kinds of matters relating to art and photography." How did major art dealers of that time conduct their business? Sala, one of the biggest in Leiden, frequented the workshops of the representatives of the Hague School (Haagse School), and sold their works in Scotland, from where they went to Canada. Or Van Wisselingh, who went to the United States to organise selling exhibitions with painters of The Hague School.

One generation later, **art with a capital 'A' arrived**, and Douwes could measure himself with the finest of the profession. **The sixth Evert** (1888-1971) in a row who was to see this happen, first went to the German town of Breslau in 1910 before entering his father's business. It so happened that the renowned art dealer Wenzel from Breslau was in Amsterdam, and Henri asked him if he had an internship for his son. That period of working as a volunteer would introduce Evert to Central Europe and its art. The now rechristened Polish town of Wroclaw (Breslau) was then a distinguished town of science and culture. There, but also in nearby Dresden and Leipzig, members of the Polish and Hungarian nobility bought much of their art. In the end, Evert was to stay there for two and a half years, a period that would give him much knowledge and love for the old masters.

Evert VI by W.G. Hofker, 1956

Hendrick Avercamp

KUNSTHANDEL
GEBR·DOUWES
Our gallery sign, c. 1930

The period that followed, spent in Frankfurt with the world famous Haenfstangel, would prove to be of lasting significance to his interest in documenting art. Haenfstangel was the first photographer to come up with a method of producing perfect reproductions of paintings in larger quantities, the famous brownish prints (carbon transfers). To this end, he went to all the European museums and art dealers, photographing the whole of western art spanning the period from 1200 to 1800. The photos were printed in dark-brown hues on thin paper of approximately A4 size. It fascinated Evert, who saw it as a means of increasing his knowledge. At his departure, he received 10.000 of these photo images as a gift, and they became the basis of the present library. Once again, here was a Douwes generation that made a case for documentation, and would hand it on to the next generation. In 1918, he wrote to a trainee being considered for employment about his future activities: *"Bookkeeping at present is simply structured, but we are lagging behind. Once we have caught up, there will be much time for talking with possible visitors, setting up a card index filing system, and the collection of Old-Amsterdam. I have laid the basis for a technical library (still modest, though) that will serve every member of the firm."*

When, a couple of years later, Evert opened his London branch, he met Sir Robert Witt (1872 – 1952). A passionate man, who collected and catalogued art reproductions of paintings and also of sculptures. Together, they improved and perfected both of their systems. The Douwes archive was in long rows of green boxes containing grey folders. The traditional green boxes later formed the start of the DeWitt Library, a part of the famous London *Courtauld Institute of Art*.

In the Netherlands, we have the *Rijksbureau voor Kunsthistorische Documentatie – RKD* ('National Bureau of Art Historical Documentation'). Of this respected institute, too, Douwes was the one who laid the basis. He had met Professor Cornelis Hofstede de Groot (1863-1930), a well-known art historian, publicist, collector, and expert in the field of 17th century Dutch painting. Already in 1895, the basis for Hofstede's interest in art documentation was laid when, as an assistant to Mauritshuis director Bredius, he made the museum catalogue. Many years later at Douwes's, he saw the 'green boxes', which resulted in an identical setup of his own art archive. Eventually, in 1926, he donated this archive to the nation, and formed the basis for the founding of the *RKD*.

Douwes Sr.: "My father always bought three catalogues when at an exhibition. He kept one, and the remaining two were completely cut up. Thus, of each artist he collected as many pictures of his work as possible. In this way, with the help of the whole family, the library grew to such proportions that, in the eighties, we sold to the Getty Museum those foreign art movements and art schools that we did not do business in. At present, we focus on archiving only those that we do business in."

Minne Bakker, 69 years with Dou[w]

Having worked in Frankfurt for six months, the time for the real work at his father's in Amsterdam started in 1913. One of the first things Evert initiated was a reduction of the activities not directly related to painting. Costume dolls, photos, and all sorts of 'bric á brac', as his son now calls it, left the premises. Meanwhile, father Henri had grown older and considered it just fine that his son wanted to approach things differently. What remained was of course the restoration work, but from now on the frames were to be made elsewhere. There were good Italian frame makers in the Kalverstraat, such as Lurasco and Grisanti, who for centuries had handed down their craft. The art of calligraphy, once started by Evert (V) in the 19th century, was still only practiced to meet the need of making stylish name plaques to go with the paintings.

Evert Douwes Sr.: 'I remember how my old restoration tutor Minne Bakker, employed by us for 69 years, had to go to Wynand Focking's (Amsterdam distillery) bar. On those occasions, he went to fetch for restoration the old round bottles with their lavish, multi-coloured inscriptions. Already in the 19th century, calligraphy was used by my great-uncle to decorate those bottles. At present, they are still in the bodega, as ornamental bottles. Eventually, the Douwes calligraphy resulted in the Amsterdam script letter, still being taught at art colleges. "Johann Wilhelm Beekmann Sr. (1867-1918), employed by my grandfather during 25 years until 1906, trained his son Johann (1895-1986) who became the famous letter writer. He beautified this script letter, which can still be seen on the name plaques of the many paintings in the Frans Hals Museum at Haarlem."

World War I erupted, and Evert had to take up arms. He was quartered in Fort Kadijk, in the province of North Holland. Though he came home regularly for the weekends, business for that reason could not yet be pursued vigorously. During the war (1914-1918), the art trade slumped. It was made even worse when in 1916 the government slapped a 'luxury tax' of 3% on the possession of art. Father Henri, though, continued to run the gallery, and was still busy writing the history of Amsterdam. After two years, Evert was allowed to leave the military early, because he had to provide for two families. From then on, the old masters were gradually introduced into the gallery. Bought at Dutch auction houses and sold only to Dutch customers, because the war had caused the market to become very domestically orientated.

Johann Beekmann (1895-1986)

After the war, Evert approached business on a grand scale, and in 1919 they moved to a large building at Rokin 46, in which all disciplines could now be housed. Evert Douwes Sr.: "I still remember, as a small boy of five, the little ferry

Inventory log-book, c.1920's

Gerard van Spaendonck

Willem van de Velde the Younger

VI with 'Paatje and Maatje' Douwes

Vincent van Gogh

that crossed the Rokin, which at the time was still a canal". Douwes was one of the first to settle there. Antique dealer Delaunoy, and art dealer Van Wisselingh already had. In the prosperous twenties, the Rokin, with its approximately twenty-five fine art and antique dealers, became the art boulevard of the Netherlands. From that time onwards, Douwes focused on purely 17th century Flemish and Dutch masters, the Hague School, and Romanticism. His first foreign customers after WW1 were predominantly Germans that he had acquainted when working with Wenzel in Breslau. Laurens van Dam was such a customer. A Jewish collector from Berlin, who – just as many of his kinsmen – was very interested in art. They, too, became Evert's customers and could add a Dutch master to their collections, when in Amsterdam.

On the new premises, the first selling exhibition was organised in 1920.

In 1925, Evert Jr.'s grandfather had gone to hotel Huis ter Duin in Noordwijk, where, in the adjacent coach house, he exhibited for the 'cream of the crop', then spending their holidays there. In general, however, the paintings stayed put in Amsterdam, and there was little going on tours.

Owing to the recovering economy, the Dutch art world was very active in the aftermath of WW1. The period from 1920 to 1928 turned into an important art market with many international buyers. In that time, with the arts prospering, there were a number of Amsterdam lead players. Auctioneers Frederik Muller, as the only quality auction house, played an important role. (Douwes had succeeded in buying all of their old catalogues, which are an important part of the present library). In 1911, the *Vereniging van Handelaren in Oude Kunst – VHOK*' ('Dutch Art and Antique Dealers Association') was established, and in 1919, Evert was one of the founders of the "*Nederlandse Kunstkopersbond – NKB*" ('Dutch Art Buyers Association'). This association, purely intended for art dealers in contemporary art, aimed at promoting the art from 1850 to 1919 and beyond, and organised exhibitions to this end. Other members were a.o. Sala, Du Bois, Elbert Jan van Wisselingh (on the Rokin), Buffa (in the Kalverstraat), art dealer C.M. van Gogh (on the Rokin) - called 'uncle Cor' by the painter Vincent - and Caramelli & Tessaro.

Douwes Sr.: 'my father was always on the board, and even I have for a long time been their secretary. I believe it is now in a dormant state."

There was the passionate collector Frits Lugt (1884-1970), who, even before finishing secondary school, was already employed by Frederik Muller and acquired a vast knowledge while there. In addition, using his keen eye and excellent visual memory, and together with his wealthy wife, he built an imposing collection of paintings and drawings. Eventually, he housed his collection in the Fondation Custodia, part of the Institut Néerlandais in Paris. In the seventies,

Douwes Gallery exhibition, Huis ter Duin, Noordwijk 1925

Amsterdam, the Rokin with ferry-boat, c. 1930

Frans van Mieris

Rokin, 'Spiegelzaal', c. 1930

George Hendrik Breitner

Obituary of Henri Douwes, 1938

Evert Douwes Jr. was to make descriptions of a part of this art collection, which he also studied to improve his knowledge.

Douwes maintained close ties with another Amsterdam art gallery, namely that of Jacques Goudstikker. The man, whose heirs now demand the return of his paintings, was the third generation of their art gallery. Between the two was a lively exchange of paintings. The name Goudstikker frequently appears in the buying and selling records dating from the early twenties. In 1922, for example, Douwes sold to him a church interior from Emmanuel de Witte for 1.750 guilders, acquired in 1921 for 1.542 guilders. In 1923, he sold him a Davis Bles, 'Ora et Labora' for 350 guilders, which he had acquired in 1921 for 300 guilders.

Goudstikker also focused on early Italian art, a school still not so well known in the Netherlands. He approached business on a grand scale, and, after buying Nyenrode Castle, he organised gorgeous exhibitions there, with lavishly illustrated catalogues. Douwes Sr.: 'He was probably influenced by the art dealer Duveen, who was earning richly in New York and spending it in circles of rich industrialists such as Randolph Hearst.

Goudstikker was the man of the grand gesture, and could easily be wide off the mark. My father cautioned him once when he wanted to sell a Hercules Seghers still life for a lot of money. Later, it turned out to be part of a bigger canvas by an Italian painter".

In 1922, a newcomer with 17th century Dutch and Flemish masters, spoken of highly by both father and son Evert, was the Pieter de Boer art gallery, established at Herengracht 512. They shared an interest in the same period of painting, and they, too, learned from each other. De Boer was the first to organise an exhibition of Dutch still lifes, including among others paintings by Willem Claesz. Heda. Evert Douwes in turn also acquired the most beautiful work of his lesser-known son Gerrit Heda, now in the collection of the Worcester Art Museum, Massachusetts. Douwes Sr.: " What I admire in De Boer is that, even in times of crisis, he continued to organise exhibitions. He was perhaps inspired by Goudstikker, who organised regular exhibitions, a.o. one of winter landscapes in 1932."

In the 18th and 19th centuries, British nobility was already buying a lot of art, among them many Dutch old masters. Of the 17th century 'fine' painter ('fijnschilder') Godfried Schalcken is known that he sold his paintings directly in England. In the twenties, London, with its prominent auction houses, became the source of old masters. That is why in 1922, Evert decided to open a London branch and went to live there, while father Henri took care of the business in Amsterdam. At a later stage, a partner, Hein Hoes, who was in charge of sales in

Amsterdam, joined the firm. Evert married Allegonda Vogt, and together they had three sons and a daughter. In an interview on his 80th birthday, he reminisced: "I also went to London in 1927 on our honeymoon. I had promised to forget about paintings for a fortnight. We went into hiding in a small hotel, and yet somebody tracked me down. The end of the story was that I came home with two Saenredams, and one Jan Steen." With Jan Steen, Evert was very familiar. "That is because of Bredius, who taught me much about him. In the prime of my life, I knew more about Jan Steen than most of my colleagues put together."

Evert VI and Gonny Douwes-V[...]

Between the two world wars, London was the Mecca for art dealers. Every week was certain to bring a 'discovery'. A canvas or panel offered in a dirty unrecognizable condition would turn out to be a great master. That discovery was sometimes only made in Amsterdam, after Evert, who lived in London for nine months a year, with his load of paintings had left for the Rokin by boat and train. Another possibility was that he thought he had bought a Van Goyen, the signature 'came off' and it turned out to be a Schoeff. Nowadays, this would be a financial disaster, but at that time the damage remained limited due to the minimal investment. Douwes Sr.: 'one could as it were still find a Van Goyen every week.' Another restorer of our firm, Jan Schutte, who was with us for 53 years, had an instinctive feel for and knowledge of 17th century painting. Evert Sr.: '...my father regularly invited him to London to do the sales together and discuss the quality of the pictures offered for sale, in order to pick the better ones for our collection...'.

Sale at Christies, London, c. 192[...]

At present, thanks to our improved knowledge, they would no longer all be considered Van Goyens. Market development was not then a priority, so the ten odd Jan van Goyens were not bought in order to stash them away for investment purposes. After all, on average they would cost 300 guilders a piece. No, you bought only the very best, for around 1.200 guilders. In addition, a lesser master in the same genre would cost just 200 guilders less. The difference between a Jan van Goyen and a Jacob Woutersz. Knijff was 120 guilders. Whenever my father considered the Knijff to be better, he would buy that one. He always bought the top segment of the lesser-known masters, and the time came when he did indeed have many customers for them. You have to educate people. Many people prefer to buy a bad painting of a great master before a quality painting of a lesser master. He did his buying not only in London, but travelled the length and breadth of Britain and Ireland. For example, he found a Holbein portrait in Ireland, sold it to the textile magnate Van Heeck. At present it is in the Rijksmuseum Twente (National Gallery of Twente), in the Dutch town of Enschede."

Jan Schutte, 53 years with Douw[...]

He must have told many a fascinating tale about his 'discoveries' in the London of that time. When putting that question to (the present) Evert Douwes Sr., he tells somewhat ruefully that at the start of the sixties he had failed to record his

Jan Steen

Frans Hals

Barend C. Koekkoek

Johan B. Jongkind

Jubilee exhibition, 1955

father's stories. He does still remember some of the family's 'discoveries', though. For example, one of the most beautiful Saenredams, the one of the Maria Church in Utrecht; an important Frans Hals portrait and a Rembrandt landscape; a Jan Steen sold to the Rotterdam shipowner Goudriaan and now in the Metropolitan in New York; two Aert de Gelder paintings, which are in Melbourne (Australia) and in the J.P.Getty Museum in Malibu (USA); one of the most beautiful Hendrick Avercamps now in Toledo, donated by a Canadian banker they once sold it to; important still lifes by Willem Heda and Pieter Claesz., acquired by the amiable US Senator John Heinz, are now on loan at the National Gallery in Washington. The contents of the acquisition and sales records of the twenties, which fortunately do indeed still exist, would be the dream of each and every art dealer living in 2005. A selection: *'Summer landscape' by B.C. Koekkoek, bought in 1923 for 975 guilders, sold in 1923 to one Dreesmann for 1.500 guilders. A 'Summer landscape' by Andreas Schelfhout, bought from Frederik Muller in 1921 for 352 guilders and sold in the same year for 650 guilders. A 'Merry company' by Jan Steen, bought in 1921 for 16.104 guilders and sold in 1921 for 25.000 guilders. A watercolour by Jacob Maris, 'View of a harbour', bought for 203 guilders and sold for 300 guilders. 'Work at the farm' by Jozef Israëls, bought in 1921 for 1450 guilders and sold in 1923 voor 2.880 guilders. A panel by Peter Paul Rubens, "Christ as gardener', bought in 1922 for 12.250 guilders, sold in 1923 for 19.000 guilders.*

It paints a picture of the world of the father of Douwes Sr. "There was a massive supply, you travelled a lot, and with a lot of knowledge made many discoveries. In those times, my father knew more than most of the others. I myself now know more than he did. I would have loved to work in his period of time with my present knowledge. I would have made a lot of money."

The 'crash' of 1929 forced the closure of the London branch in 1932. The family returned to Holland and settled in Bussum, where in the meantime father Henri had also moved. In Amsterdam too, times were hard, with occasionally slim profit margins. Douwes Sr.: "In 1928, my father bought a magnificent Aert van de Neer for 10.000 guilders, and in 1937 he was offered 2.000 guilders for it, which he accepted because it enabled him to at least pay his employees. Some twelve years ago, I sold it on behalf of the owner's son for 300.000 guilders."
Those who kept buying were the physicians. In the crisis years, they were taxed only twenty percent. A group with a lot of affinity for art, culturally grounded, and still able to build a collection. With a sense of nostalgia, Douwes Sr. speaks of the time of collectors such as Ten Kate, Van Heeck, Heldring. And of the affinity for art and culture which has become so much less, the taste that has also become much more internationally oriented. 'I remember an important sale in 1934. To one of our loyal customers, my father sold five paintings for 18.000 guilders.

One of those five was a Van Goyen, and the other a Jan Steen. Later, I saw pictures again of these two paintings; just the two of them would now fetch 600.000 to 700.000 Euros.

In the second half of the thirties, Douwes and de Boer had many German customers who avoided the Jewish Goudstikker, because of the already latent German anti-semitism. When WW2 erupted, trading with the regular German art dealers went on till about the first half of 1942. Douwes Sr.: 'Most of the important art dealers initially still traded with their regular German colleagues such as Plietsch and Hofer, until they got wind of the fact that the paintings were in turn sold straight to the ranks of the German high command. From then on, they notified each other whenever German art dealers came to Amsterdam. Then it was up to you; my father took care not to be in the gallery and stopped doing business. During the war, food became a problem. My father solved it in part by exchanging his paintings. I remember a beautiful painting of the 17th century painter Frans Snijders in our house. It was exchanged for a bale of sugar and many other food items. Relatives, too, had to eat to stay alive, and it meant that in May 1945 the gallery stock had been reduced from a few hundred to eventually eight paintings. After the war, we were not involved in selling former confiscated Jewish art possessions. On the contrary, our large safe was filled with paintings entrusted to us by two Jewish owners. Everything was returned to them or to their families. In addition, together with the directors (Roëll and Sanberg) of the *Rijksmuseum* ('National Art Gallery') and the *Stedelijk Museum* ('Amsterdam Municipal Art Gallery'), my father was also active in the foundation *Nederlands Kunstbezit* ('Dutch National Heritage Collection'), which tracked down Dutch works of art in German possession.

In 1948, at the request of the Ministry of Justice, Evert wrote a report on the art trade during the war years. In 1943, six times as much as in 1940 was paid for works of the Old Masters, and even eight times as much for paintings from the Romantic School period. After 1944, however, prices declined sharply. In about 1947, they had dropped some 70% for the Old and Romantic Masters, and 40% for the Moderns.

Winning his bet in 1943

In 1947, during the courtcase dealing with forgeries by Han van Meegeren, Gebr. Douwes with photos and written records was instrumental in proving thay the underlying painting of the so-called *Last Supper* - bought by D.G. van Beuningen, and now in the museum Boymans-Van Beuningen, Rotterdam - was in fact a pristine, large canvas by Abraham Hondius *Tableau of a Hunting scene*. X-ray publications showed the underlying image, which is identical to the plate of the original painting by Hondius.

Brotherly spirit in the inner circle of art dealers during the time of war can best be illustrated with the joint visit of Evert (1888) and his colleague D.A.Hoogendijk

A. Hondius, underpainting of Van Me

Evert VII with Ochtervelt, 1963

Opening Delft Art Fair, 1964

Delft Fair exhibitors, 1964

Evert VII, by L. van Dijk, 1969

to an auction of Fredrik Muller's in 1943. Both professionals placed a bet on the exact result of its sales proceeds. As it turned out, Evert was right on the mark and won it. Soon afterwards, he was presented with a symbolic token of their esteem: three of the finest cigars together with a framed document handwritten and signed by the losers of this bet.

The 6th of March 1946 was the day Evert Douwes Sr. entered his father's employ. About this he says, "After the crisis and the war period, we were flooded by restoration work. My father said 'come and join me right after school to learn the craft.' It was not my number one wish, but the restoration work fascinated me to such an extent that I did it for ten years. Restoring was and is important to us, because you make new contacts. People need a valuation, or want to sell the painting after its restoration, or give it on consignment. The latter is interesting, for the art trade prefers to purchase works of art from private collections and in the auction room that have not circulated too widely. Since 1991, we also have a restoration studio in Friesland, where my son Erick (1956) works."

It did not stop at restoration, because once every fortnight during more than three years, Douwes Sr. was privately tutored in the history of art by the well-known professor Willem Vogelsang. Vogelsang was known in the art trade because of his valuations, handwritten for 25 Euros. Signature or brushstroke were thus scientifically validated, and professors were able to supplement their meagre salaries. Practical experience abroad was acquired in London and Paris, whenever father and son did the rounds of the auction houses and the dealers. In 1947, he spent much time with his godfather Karel Duits, a well-known art dealer, whose family had settled in London in the twenties.

In 1952, he married Nelleke Huf, niece of the famous Dutch photographer Paul Huf (1929-2002). Together, they had three sons (Evert-Jules, Erick-Hans, and Peter), and a daughter (Pia).

In the early fifties, Douwes Sr., who had after all fallen in love with London, really tried to establish himself in there. He did restoration work for a year, but then duty called him back to Amsterdam. His help was needed in the preparation of the 1955 Jubilee exhibition.

After celebrating the 150th anniversary – "we made a retrospective of what we had sold in those 150 years" –, Douwes Sr. was asked to take over from his father. On this, he says: "at a certain moment my father said to me 'I have seen it all'. In retrospect, I can now understand this. He had had a splendid time from 1918-1930, followed by the crisis and then WW2. This meant that he had hardly been able to do anything between 1930 and 1945. So, how do you continue from there? A reputable business, knowledge, and a number of paintings. What else can you do but to start all over again?"

Immediately after WW2, he attempted to get the business going again and in the process was asked to fill various board memberships. Buying abroad was not allowed. The Dutch art trade was forced to turn national for some years. The trade bought and sold amongst themselves, with the auction house as an important source. Paintings from private individuals were of course always being offered, or people wanted to exchange one painting for another. Trade by barter is a phenomenon of all times. Heirs less happy with the choice of their parents came and are still coming regularly to hand in objects and exchange it for something else more suited to their tastes. Douwes Sr.: 'My father negotiated intensively with the ministerial departments to obtain foreign currency for the art trade that would enable them to buy abroad, and in which he succeeded in 1948. The art trade received foreign currency to the tune of 213.820 guilders, to be divided among those firms that were internationally the most active. The *Adviesbureau voor den Kunsthandel* ("Consultancy Office for the Art Trade") was founded with its offices on my father's premises. All it did was to distribute the currencies and register the acquisitions. My father was so absorbed by this that he partly neglected his own firm.

Of course, I substituted for him during that time, but was also fully occupied doing restorations. A regular customer was the late E.J.van Wisselingh art gallery on the Rokin, for which we have done all of their restoration work during fifteen years after the war. Van Wisselingh conducted business in many French post-, pre-, and impressionists, which all of them I saw 'pass by'. This is how I acquired my knowledge of and interest in the French masters. I was longing for something different from the 19th century 'snapshots', and about 1960 I started buying my first French pre-impressionists. What fascinated me most were the precursors of the impressionists, the 'école de Barbizon'. Inspired by the Dutch 17th century landscapes of Ruysdael and Hobbema, they had gone 'outside' ('en plein-air'), to Barbizon, a hovel in the woods of Fontainebleau, south-east of Paris.'
Douwes Sr. became friends with a London art dealer, Herbert Terry-Engell, from whom he bought a lot. Together they went to Swiss auctions, where many French impressionists were sold.

In the sixties, Douwes Sr. saw prices rise through greater prosperity and an increase in knowledge; the connoisseur paid ever more for quality.
In the seventies, art as an investment started to play a role. The big names became rare and more expensive, with demand increasing and the buyer becoming more critical. Prices of lesser masters also went up, as did prices of Old Dutch and Flemish drawings, another love of Douwes Sr..
The market for drawings is much smaller than for paintings, and the big collectors live in the States. They are also the ones that have driven up prices in the past decennia. Douwes at present has a beautiful 17th century Saverij drawing costing

Evert VI, photo Paul Huf, 195

Rokin, by W.G. Hofker, 1974

Evert VII at the Rokin, c. 1990

H. Terry-Engell and Nelleke Dou

Prince Bernhard visits TEFAF, 1982

Opening Douwes in London, 1979

Cornelis Springer exh. at Douwes, 1984

Our library, Stadhouderskade, 2001

46.000 Euros. In the sixties, it would have cost 10.000 guilders, just a tenth of its present value. There was even a time when drawings cost a few guilders, as the following anecdote relates: "Though 'uncle Joh', who took all the time in the world for his study of the classical languages, did not go into the business, he did have a keen eye for it. In 1923 he came home one day carrying a drawing by Esaias van de Velde dated 1628, for which he had paid 12 guilders. My grandfather became angry, "you focus on your studies", and bought the drawing from his son. About 30 years ago, I came across the drawing and sold it to a German industrialist for 18.000 guilders. Nowadays, that Van de Velde would be worth 65.000 Euros."

In 1976, entirely in keeping with his father's tradition of always buying the top of the smaller 17th century masters, the first exhibition of just French paintings followed, 'Paysage de France', with mainly lesser-known French masters, among them many 'école de Barbizon' painters. The show with over a hundred paintings was entirely sold out.

This 'école de Barbizon', with well-known painters such as Daubigny and Rousseau, became the specialty of Douwes Sr.. Throughout the seventies, he built a considerable market for it. Yet, within the total Douwes supply, this French movement has always remained of limited size. "The genuine collectors did not come to me, but bought directly in Paris or from Van Wisselingh. In the meantime, in nearly a century, the latter had already built a worldwide reputation in the field of French great masters. Nowadays, you would go to Noortman. But for a Ruysdael, you would go to de Boer or to Douwes."

To maintain this reputation, Evert Douwes Sr. organised regular exhibitions. Senior considers the still life exhibition of 1968 one of the highlights of his career. "I had made a wonderful shop window with objects from a Steenwijk painting of 1660. The painting with the objects ranged in front of it drew crowds of viewers."

Thirty-five thousand slides of paintings are the result of shots taken since the sixties. Two-thirds is 17th century, half of which still lifes, the rest is 19th century. The library and multi-media section are famous at home and abroad. Many students find their way to them, and many a curator or museum director drops by. Douwes Sr. in fact continues what his great-grandfather started in 1905, and what the latter's son continued with an initial 10.000 carbon transfers. Senior takes about seven exposures per painting. "Putting these in a row next to each other, you can see right away whether something is good, has been restored, or is a fake, but especially can one study the ever so important brush technique. My slide collection is some sort of a hobby. I also take pictures with colleagues at fairs and such, in order to collect as much material as possible. I want to record for later generations the knowledge I have acquired. When my son wants to buy a flower still life and thinks, "is it a David de Heem or a Cornelis de Heem", he

In 2005, fifth & sixth generation Douwes Fine Art: Evert VII and Evert VIII.
(courtesy of More Than Classic, photo Freek Esser)

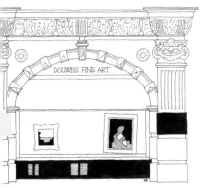

Duke Street, St. James's, London

Evert VIII in London, 1980

...ves Fine Art opens in London, 1979

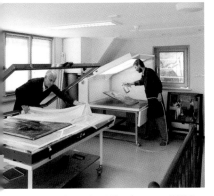

...ves restoration, St. Nicolaasga, 1992

can then go upstairs and project a number of paintings by both, and by then it should be clear to him."

It is not usual or natural that a son follows in his father's footsteps. Evert Douwes Jr. tells about his doubts and hesitations when in secondary school in the late sixties and early seventies, and about the fact that studying medecine and psychology also attracted him. When visiting customers with his father and grandfather, he did however realize that psychological insight into people and their decision-making processes did certainly play a role. Art and psychology could thus be happy partners. Evert Jr.: "I was the eldest, and as a juvenile I already sensed the presence of a background I couldn't just shake off; a background for which I already felt a sense of responsibility. My father has always left me free to make up my own mind. I had strong ties with my grandfather, a scholarly man, who told me much of his knowledge and experiences. He taught me to become aware of how much pleasure it gives to gather knowledge about art. He himself was still working in the library. My father has a phenomenal knowledge which he has handed down to me, and which he still hands on to others. He has the rare and passionate gift of wanting to share his knowledge. Armed with the insights of two generations, you then ask yourself: "how can I contribute?" It became Art History.

But first, he was enlisted in the Dutch Army, and gradually was assigned to that small army unit responsible for the protection of the Dutch national heritage. This task allowed him to familiarize himself with the hidden treasures in museum depots and private collections in some of the Royal palaces. He now continues in the Army Reserve, at present with the rank of Major.

After his studies, Evert Jr. did an internship with Eberhard Kornfeld in Bern. An outstanding firm, a combination of art gallery, auction house, and publishing company, all under the same roof. Kornfeld, an intellectual academic, was one of the greatest connoisseurs of the classical modern art of painting, a movement stretching roughly from Goya and Delacroix to Picasso and Sam Francis. In his younger years, as an internee, he had been secretary to Chagall and Picasso. Evert learnt a lot about this movement, as yet little known in the Netherlands. "Kornfeld also gave me an insight into the etchings and drawings of Rembrandt, and into modern graphics. Later on, I often went back to work for them for short periods, to prepare auctions. At a given moment, the situation was such that I lived and worked simultaneously in London and Amsterdam, and also worked in Bern for longer periods of time. At the end of the eighties, they employed me every second week. Rather hectic, but I learnt so much there!"

The next internship was once again a matter of just gathering knowledge: studying the collection of Frits Lugt in the Institut Néerlandais in Paris. Evert stayed with the well-known Belgian art dealer Leegenhoek. With him, he made his first deal after making a 'discovery'. It so happened that he found a 17th century painting by David Teniers, which Leegenhoek was willing to buy from him. With the commission money earned, he could pay for his stay in Paris, and he learnt that looking closely at the collections of colleagues could be profitable. Where he really had his eyes popping was in the English country houses and stately homes during a one-year course at Sotheby's in London, which came next. Apart from the theory, the fifty students together with three experts went to English country homes laden with art. "Where normally speaking there would be stretched rope barriers, we could step over them and handle everything."

In July 1979, the Douwes firm took over the lease from an old acquaintance that wanted to retire from his art dealing business. In Duke Street, they were "back in town" after 47 years. Evert Jr.: "My father had always wanted to return to London, but the roots were in Amsterdam, after all. It thrilled him to bits that we were 'back'. It produced new business and new collectors from all over the world. Germans, for example, who until the nineties had been avid collectors, had the idea that 'if you made your choice in London as the art centre, then you would have made the best choice possible. Or private individuals, who offered a painting exclusively to you, because they had a distant Dutch relative somewhere along the line."

In 1986, Evert Jr. for the first time saw a Russian art exhibition. That certainly was not an everyday happening in London, but in the Soviet Union of Gorbatchev 'glasnost' was the order of the day, and thus the world could get to know social realistic art, a movement that reached its pinnacle in the period 1940-1970. "I was amazed at the quality, the colours, and the humour of these paintings. I had thought that the 'grey communism' would also be visible on these canvases. The opposite was true, and I was sold forthwith. The prices were very interesting and ranged from 500 to 5000 pounds sterling. Not much later, I bought my first Russian painting at an auction. Through this acquisition, I came into contact with British people married to Russian wives or having other links with Russia, and thus succeeded in building a network enabling me to buy good Russian art.

Each generation of our firm has added something new, and for me it was 'the Russians'. How the market would develop I did not know at the time, but before long I had an international clientele for this art. It is funny to see that the customer always comes off best; it is he who has 'time' on his side. At the moment of buying, it may be a hefty sum for them, but twenty, thirty years later they come and thank me for having sold it to them."

The Grosvenor House Art and Antiques Fair, held for the first time in 1934, was the model for the *Vereniging van Handelaren in Oude Kunst – VHOK* when

Boerinnen in pasteltint

Newspaper clipping NRC, Dec. 20

Waldorf-Astoria exh., New York, 1

Douwes gallery at Stadhouderskade,

Evert VII & VIII with Erick-Ha

22

vert VIII with a Joos de Momper

Erick-Hans restoring in Friesland

toration studio in Amsterdam, 2004

at the gallery on Friday afternoon

organising their first fair at the Prinsenhof in Delft in 1948. This *Oude Kunst en Antiekbeurs* ('Art and Antiques Fair') would eventually grow into a fair of high quality enjoying an excellent reputation at home and abroad. In the end, the location proved an obstacle to its further growth. In 1974, a small group of young art dealers, among them Douwes Sr., started actively looking for another location. At the insistence of the old guard, it had to be at a distance of 200 kilometres from Delft. This resulted in the first Pictura in Maastricht in 1975, an event that Douwes Sr. and his extensive network had played a major role in. He is now justifiably proud of the fact that as a co-founder, he was at the birth of The European Fine Art Fair, the prestigious annual TEFAF.

Together, father and son witnessed and supported the launch of the Dutch art magazine *Tableau* in the late seventies. And to broaden their international client base, together with five other Dutch dealers, they were the first to show their own presentation of first class art and antiques in the Waldorf Astoria Hotel in New York, in 1982 and 1983.

Evert Jr.: "I view the ever greater role played by the auction houses as market places of the art world, as an important aspect in the thirty years that I have been active so far. I have witnessed from nearby the coming into existence of the PAN (Dutch National Fair in Amsterdam) in 1986, and the great success of the TEFAF. They provide a counterbalance to the big international auction houses that, on a worldwide scale and with a great deal of public relations, absorb everything. Fairs will always remain important, as they were in the 16th and 17th centuries. To maintain their high quality, much of the knowledge of the art galleries is needed. But much of the knowledge accumulated by former generations is gradually disappearing. Expertise is being handed down, but too little. What we are already witnessing is that the next generation now go to University, absorb a lot of theory, but (sometimes) lack the practical knowledge resulting from frequently and actually handling the paintings. The very important paintings are simply no longer offered for sale. In the sixties, my father could buy two Van Goyens a month, in the seventies hardly one a month, and if I now come across two in a year, I can count myself lucky if I am able to buy one."

He remembers an anecdote about his father buying a rare and early Jan van Goyen abroad, monogrammed and dated 1623. "During the late fifties and sixties, my Dad travelled throughout Europe by car. When he returned with his discovery and crossed the Dutch border, the very first car he passed had the incredible number plate of 'VG-16-23'. He laughed so hard, this just could not be a fluke …. now could it!"

Evert Jr. married his first wife, Ingeborg, in London in 1988. Sadly, she later died of cancer at the age of 38. Together, they had two daughters (Alexandra and

Olivia), and a son (Evert-Anthony). Recently, Evert Jr. married Ingeborg's younger sister Jeanneke, thus once again making the family complete.

At the start of the nineties, the market stagnated, and once again Evert Jr. decided to join the family firm fulltime. He shouldered the entire organisation of moving the firm from the Rokin to the Stadhouderskade. In 1994, in this accessible property, all disciplines once again regained their own proper surroundings. On its walls still hang 500 years of painting, the same that junior's predecessors also dealt in. Can it continue like this, unchanged and in a difficult art market, with high prices for rarely available art? Evert Jr.: "Loyal collectors have become less in number, because of lack of time, the influence of interior decorating, the accessibility of auction houses, and the knowledge factor helped by fast means of communication. People choose on colour and for decoration purposes, and no longer choose a painting with an interesting iconography. Ten, twenty years ago, there were still enough people in Holland who were genuinely collecting. They took the time to drop by. For two hours, you relished the joy of discussing and viewing a number of paintings. And then, you would sell one of them."

Family photo by Paul Huf, 199?

Evert: "Why continue? Is tradition important? Is that a reason to stay on? Can I myself go on with it, just as ten, thirty, fifty years ago? After all, aren't we a kind of institution? With a restoration workshop as an important component of our business, a wide-ranging documentation system and library, and five centuries of painting? A two centuries old company is not something to discard just like that. We have always been there for the art, the craftsmanship, and the passion. We want to be able to sell art for everybody. It means we are more intensely occupied with our trade, and also do not always have the means to buy that great name.

Evert VII decorated, 1998

Evert can be jealous of his father's period, from about 1955 to 1975. "There was still sufficient supply, and you did not yet have to make choices from those five hundred years of painting that the firm houses. The present market situation is different. As a result, some art dealers have changed course and chosen to focus on just the great names. Or, on just the French impressionists and the old masters, both groups enjoying international interest. But, in an old firm such as ours, the passions of our predecessors with their contemporary art or topography have been handed down to us.

Three generations 'Evert' in the fi?

So, when some of our colleagues have problems hanging a 17th century Hendrick Maartensz. Sorgh next to a 19th century Corot, because they think it is unorthodox, we do indeed still return home with a gorgeous Cornelis Bega, a Maris or an Eversen, which we are perhaps able to buy once a year, and which

Stadhouderskade 40, c. 1885

Evert VIII during Vetting

Evert VIII and Jeanneke, 2005

Rembrandt revival, 2005

...wes, neighbour of the Rijksmuseum

we cannot let pass, because it so happens that we may have decided to buy only great names such as Jan Davidsz. de Heem, Jongkind and Springer, now can we?

That is what we are juggling and wrestling with. Personally, I feel that good and artistic qualities in Art are of all ages. They just need time to prove themselves. And, in my opinion, once the following generations have confirmed these important qualities, there are hardly any boundaries between the different periods and they can indeed be combined together."

How do you chart a new course so that a next generation can in turn earn its keep? There is a growing role to play for the Internet. A steadily growing number of people visit the Douwes site, and ask for information. More and more, even China is looking our way and it is funny that the market provided an answer here: participate in the Shanghai Art Fair of 2005.

Evert Jr.: "The Chinese are not yet ready for the old Dutch and Flemish masters, but they are for the lesser French impressionists. We still stock them, despite much hard thinking on the subject. They also appreciate our Russian social realistic art; a movement that has been well received in the Netherlands, but with much less spontaneity than abroad. It is affordable, and matches our aspiration to have works of art for everybody. From an international perspective, my expectations are high here. With these Russian paintings, we hope to tap a new generation of art buyers, and at the same time, with our experience spanning two centuries, we want to show the good examples of five centuries of painting."

Rembrandt is a great love of Douwes Jr.: "when I studied abroad in the seventies, I was nicknamed after him. I remember coming from the 'in' place of Amsterdam looking like a hippy with long hair and a beard, making drawings in the marvellous Victoria & Albert Museum in London. My fellow students and professors felt I looked like him. We even share the same astrological sign".

But his catching interest really goes back to the days of his internship with Kornfeld in Bern. As a result, an extensive network has gradually grown enabling him to organise a Jubilee exhibition of Rembrandt prints.

Invitation to our Jubilee exhibition *200 years Douwes Fine Art*, Dec. 2005 - Feb. 2006

Brief Version of the Douwes family tree

Walraven Jansz. Douwe - wine merchant (born in Antwerpen)
grandfather of Evert Abr. Douwdesse

Abraham Evers - wool-carder (born 1661 in Leiden)
father of Evert Abr. Douwdesse

Evert Abrahamsz. Douwdesse (born 1685 in Leiden)
named after his grandfather and father, whom baptized
this Evert together in the 'Hooglandse kerk' in Leiden

Evert Douwes II - shipwright and restorer (born 1708 in Leiden)

Evert Douwes III - shipwright and restorer (born 1760 in Amsterdam)

Hendrik Douwes - restorer and art dealer (born 1784 in Amsterdam)
registered the Douwes Fine Art Gallery in 1805

Evert Douwes IV - art dealer (born 1809 in Amsterdam)

Evert Douwes V - art dealer (born 1843 in Amsterdam)
established Douwes Brothers in 1875,
together with his younger brother Henri

Henricus Douwes - restorer and art dealer (born 1850 in Amsterdam)
established Douwes Brothers in 1875,
together with his older brother Evert V

Evert Douwes VI - art dealer (born 1888 in Amsterdam)

Evert Douwes VII - restorer and art dealer (born 1928 in London)

Evert Douwes VIII - art dealer born (1953 in Amsterdam)
together with his younger brother Erick-Hans, they
again make the next pair of 'Douwes Brothers' since 1982

Erick-Hans Douwes - restorer (born 1956 in Amsterdam)
as a restorer, he joined his older brother
in the family business in 1982

Evert-Anthony Douwes IX - a future generation !! (born 1991 in London)

"The past should be a springboard, not a sofa"

(Harold Macmillan)

MASTER PAINTINGS
DRAWINGS
WATERCOLOURS

"Art completes what nature cannot bring to a finish.
The artist gives us knowledge of nature's unrealized ends."

(Aristotle)

JAN de BEER and Studio (circa 1475 - Antwerp - circa 1528)
"Adoration of the Magi and a Vista with a landcape"
Oil on panel: 71 x 56,5 cm

Provenance: from a Belgian private collection.
Literature: Max Friedländer has managed to bring some order into a large body of anonymous Antwerp paintings that had been gradually gathered under the name of '*Herri met de Bles*'. He has identified some anonymous 'Masters' (such as the Master of the Von Groote Adoration, the Master of the Antwerp Adoration, etc.), and only a few by name, of which Jan de Beer is the best-known artist. Others include Jan Gossart, and Jan Wellens de Cock. In Max Friedländer, "Early Netherlandish Painting", 1974, Vol.XI, we can find some examples of De Beer's works that are very closely related to our painting (Plates 8 - 14). Especially no.9 "Altarpiece of the Adoration", in the Pinacoteca di Brera, Milan; and no.15 "Joseph with the Flowering Staff", at the Barber Institute of Fine Art, Birmingham.
Notes: This painting is a typical and fine example of Antwerp Mannerism. Jan de Beer was considered to be one of the most talented of a group of artists active from 1500 until circa 1530. They produced flamboyant pieces, which were very popular on the local and foreign art markets.

D<small>AVID</small> V<small>INCKBOONS</small> I (Malines 1576 - 1632 Amsterdam)
"Elegant Company making music in a Park"
Oil on panel: 38 x 64 cm; remnants of a signature, and to be dated circa 1615-1617.

Provenance: from a private Belgian collection.
Notes: He was a painter of landscapes, religious and genre scenes. A pupil of his father's, he settled in Middelburg in 1586, married Agnieta van Loon in Leeuwarden in 1602, and together they had six children. David I probably taught Gillis d'Hondecoeter and Esaias van de Velde. He was influenced by Jan Brueghel and Roelant Savery. The artist embraced the dynamism of Peter Paul Rubens's heroic landscapes. The turbulent forest scenery became animated by many elegant people, whose role became increasingly important. This painting was most likely painted during Vinckboons' stay in Amsterdam.

JAN BRUEGHEL the younger (1601- Antwerp - 1678)
and HENDRICK van BALEN (c. 1575 - Antwerp - 1632)
"Diana and her Nymphs Resting after the Hunt"
Oil on panel: 61,5 x 94,5 cm.

Provenance: from a private French collection.
Notes: In seventeenth-century Flanders, the phenomenon of two or more artists collaborating in one picture was the rule rather than the exception.
In the present work, the landscape and animals were painted by Jan Brueghel the Younger, while the figures are by Hendrick van Balen.
Jan Brueghel knew van Balen from childhood. Jan's father also used to work with van Balen. The first examples of collaboration between
Jan the Younger and van Balen predate the former's travels to Italy in about 1622. When after, his father's death in 1625, Jan the Younger
returned to Antwerp, they resumed using each other's qualities even more extensively than before. After his return to Antwerp, Jan Brueghel
continued to use his father's compositions as a point of departure.
The arrangement of the landscape in our picture is based on an earlier painting on the same subject by Jan Brueghel I, Hendrick van Balen,
and Frans Snyders. From 1625 to 1632, van Balen and the younger Brueghel realized a number of landscapes showing the goddess Diana,
her nymphs, and their catch of the hunt. Van Balen's figures are painted in an amazingly spirited manner, displaying the spontaneous brushwork
that is so typical of his later works. Our picture is to be dated at circa 1630.

JOHANNES van der AST (Middelburg before 1593 - after 1616)
"A Still Life with various Flowers in a Glass, a Shell and a Butterfly"
Oil on panel: 27,5 x 18,5 cm.

Provenance: from a private French collection, where it had stayed in the same family ever since the 19th century.
Expertise: Dr Claus Grimm has assembled a small group of paintings with particular characteristics under Johannes van der Ast's name. Some of them had been wrongly attributed to Ambrosius Bosschaert, Balthasar van der Ast, and others. The present work is dateable to circa 1610, and is one of the earliest examples of the flower piece tradition that Jan Brueghel the Elder invented.
Notes: The present painting is a free and artistic replica of a work by Jan Brueghel the Elder, now in the Staedelsches Kunstinstitut, Frankfurt. Fred Meijer has demonstrated that this small painting remained in Bosschaert's studio after he had acquired it. Here, it served as a model for a generation of Middelburg painters, with some of the flowers and cyclamen leaves being repeated in other flower pieces by a number of hands active in Bosschaert's circle. Johannes van der Ast, was the elder brother of Balthasar van der Ast, a son of Hans van der Ast and a pupil of Ambrosius Bosschaert the Elder, his brother-in-law.

ABRAHAM de VERWER (before 1600 – Amsterdam - 1650)
"Shipping near Haarlem, with cardplayers on a raft, the village of Spaarndam to the right"
Oil on panel: 36 x 46,5 cm; to be dated circa 1615-1617.

Provenance: from a Belgian private collection.
Notes: Judging by the colours and the highly placed horizon, this painting is clearly very early in date. In the background, against the skyline, we can make out the St.Bavo Cathedral of Haarlem. The flags can be recognized as the "Oranje, Blanje, Bleu" flag (later to become the national Dutch Red,White, and Blue), and the double eagle of the Habsburg empire (on the merchant vessel)

DAVID TENIERS the Younger (Antwerp 1610 – 1690 Brussels)
"A Barn Scene with an old man courting a young woman, and a group of peasants conversing in the background"
Oil on canvas: 53,5 x 69,5 cm; signed "D.Teniers"on the box (l.c.), and dated '1681'on the barrel.

Provenance: collection of the Duke of Orleans, 1798; a private English collection; from a private Dutch collection.
Literature: this is most probably the painting described by John Smith in his Catalogue Raisonné, London 1831, Vol.III, under no.372, where the dimensions are incorrectly stated as square.
Exhibition: Leeuwarden, Fries Museum, 'Van Jan Steen tot Jan Sluijters, De smaak van Douwes', from Nov.1998 until Feb.1999, cat.no.22, with ill.
Notes: A young woman and a male companion are engaged in conversation. She is smoking a typical 'Gouda' clay pipe and holding a Berkemeyer glass in her right hand. A little white dog sits trustingly by the girl's side. From a window at the top, an older lady observes the couple. Above her head an owl, the ancient symbol of wisdom. Could she be the girl's mother, secretly observing what is going on? The presence of the dog indicates a form of trust and fidelity. Is the young man putting the young woman to a test of courtship? And might the dog indicate her being faithful and not giving in to his advances? To the right in the background is a group of merry peasants, in front of an open fireplace, possibly speculating about the outcome of the couple's conversation.

BARTHOLOMEUS BREENBERGH (Deventer 1598 - 1657 Amsterdam)
"A Coastal Landscape with Saul after the Conversion"
Oil on canvas: 65 x 140,5 cm; signed and dated 1633 (on the rock).

Provenance: Richard Feigen & Co, New York, 1974; private collection, The Hague; Dr and Mrs Richard W. Levy, New Orleans.
Literature: M. Roethlisberger, New York 1981, p.65, no.154 & ill; "Bartholomeus Breenburgh: The Paintings", by M. Roethlisberger in 'The Burlington Magazine' Vol.CXXXIII, London, 1981, pp. 426-27
Exhibition: Montreal, Museum of Fine Arts, "Italian Recollections: Dutch Painters of the Golden Age", 1990, cat. by Fr. Duparc and Linda Graif, no.22, with ill.; New York, Richard L.Feigen & Co., "Bartholomeus Breenbergh", 1991, with cat. by M. Roethlisberger, cat.no.10, p.28 & ill.; The Israel Museum, Jerusalem, "Landscape of the Bible", 2000-2001 (as the only privately owned painting); London, Dulwich Picture Gallery, "Dutch Italianates", 2002; Birmingham, The Barber Institute of Fine Arts, "Bartholomeus Breenbergh", October 2004-January 2005, and The Hague, Bredius Museum, February-May 2005, cat. no. 5, p. 38 with ill. on p. 39.
Notes: After serving an apprenticeship in the Netherlands, Breenbergh moves to Italy in 1619, where he establishes a reputation as a masterly landscape draughtsman, and as a painter of pastoral scenes. Together with Cornelis van Poelenburgh (1594/5-1667), who was in Rome between 1617 and 1627, he was among the founding members of the 'Schildersbent' ('association of painters') or 'Bentvueghels' ('birds of a feather') - an association of Northern artists residing in Rome, which was founded in 1623. Upon his return to Amsterdam in about 1629, he introduces important historical subjects into his classical landscapes, and became a painter of monumental history pictures in the manner of the precursors of Rembrandt. Our painting was done in 1633, the same year Breenbergh married his wife, who came from a family of merchants.

JAN DAVIDSZ. de HEEM (Utrecht 1606 - 1684 Antwerp)

"Pronk Still Life with a Silver Cup and Cover, an overturned Silver Gilt Cup Holder, Fruit in a Basket, Peaches, a Ham, Figs, Cherries, Crabs and Lemons on Pewter Plates, Shrimps and Wine Glasses on a partly draped Table"

Oil on canvas: 88 x 120,5 cm; fully signed on the large column; dateable to c. 1645.

Provenance: collection Sir Richard V. Sutton Bt.; by descent to F. Chaplin, London 1855; with Richard Green Gallery, cat. 1971, no.6 & ill.; sale Paul Brandt, Amsterdam, 1972; with art dealer F.G. Bosiak, Frankfurt (Weltkunst no.48, 1978); with Waterman Gallery, Amsterdam, cat. 1979, no.9 & ill.; a private Dutch collection; from a foreign collection.

Expertise: Fred Meijer, in a letter of 18 October 2004: "the signature, the quality of the composition, and the certitude with which the objects are placed do not leave any doubt about the authorship." It is to be included in his forthcoming monograph on the De Heem family.

Literature: Greindl, 1983, no.10, p 359, no.69, p.361, no.69 & no.88; Sam Segal, "Jan Davidsz de Heem und sein Kreis", Herzog Anton Ulrich Museum, Braunschweig 1991, addendum 34A & ill.

Exhibition: Braunschweig, Herzog Anton Ulrich Museum, 1991, "Jan Davidsz de Heem und sein Kreis"; Leeuwarden, Fries Museum, 'Van Jan Steen tot Jan Sluijters, De smaak van Douwes', from Nov. 1998 until Feb. 1999, cat.no.9, with ill.

Notes: This world-famous Flemish/Dutch painter of sobre and yet often lavish still-lifes was a pupil of Balthasar van der Ast. The latter, together with his brother-in-law Ambrosius Bosschaert, formed the core of Still-life painters right after 1600 and is best known for his meticulous rendering of all kinds of materials, characteristicly highlighting the texture of goblets, silverware, glassware, lemons, oranges, and such like.

HENDRICK MARTENSZ. SORGH (circa 1611 - Rotterdam - 1670)
"Peasants Merrymaking in a Tavern, expressing the Five Senses"
Oil on panel: 37.5 x 50 cm; signed and dated 1644 (on the fireplace).

Provenance: acquired by Beriah Botfield (1807-1863) in Belgium, before 1848; in 1863 bequeathed by him to the former owners, the Thynne family of Longleat Chattels Settlement

Literature: B. Botfield, "Catalogue of Pictures in the possession of Beriah Botfield Esq. at Norton Hall", London, 1848, p.60 and B. Botfield, "Catalogue of Pictures at Norton Hall", London, 1863, p.46

Exhibition: London, British Institute, 1854, no.77

Notes: this is one of the earliest known, dated works by the artist and is a fine example of the work in Rotterdam that Sorgh established his reputation with. It is stylistically indebted to the work of Adriaen Brouwer, and David Teniers II under whom, according to Houbraken, he had trained in Antwerp. In 1659, he was elected chairman of the Rotterdam Guild.

JAN van GOYEN (Leiden 1596 - 1656 The Hague)
"River Landscape with Fishermen tending Eel baskets near a small Town"
Oil on panel: 39.5 x 60.5 cm; signed with monogram and dated on the boat lower right: VG 1640.

Provenance: private collection, Germany.
Literature: H.-U. Beck, Jan van Goyen 1596-1656, Amsterdam 1973, vol. 3, no. 700, p. 226, ill.
Notes: Jan van Goyen painted river scenes throughout his career. The present picture, dated 1640, stems from the period in which the artist used a limited and tonal colour scheme mainly consisting of browns and greys. Our painting displays a river scene set in subtle browns and yellows. It exemplifies the rich impression of colour that can still be obtained within the confines of such a palette. The harmonious balance of colour with its wide gamut of tones endorses the realism, and adds to the illusion of space in the landscape. However, Van Goyen did not just visualize an anonymous estuary. In addition, he evokes a specific mood, striking a melancholy key. The scarce beams of sunlight that shine through a break in the billowing clouds expressively illuminate the riverbank and the water surface, thus imbuing the scene with a sense of drama.

PIETER de NEYN
(1597 - Leiden - 1639)

"Elegant Company in a Landscape"
Oil on the original round panel:
diameter 28,5 cm;
signed and dated 1634.

"A Daylight Hold-up"
Oil on the original round panel:
diameter 28,5 cm;
twice signed and dated 1634 (l.l.)

a pair

Provenance: from a private collection in England
Notes: Both de Neyn and Jan van Goyen had their training in Haarlem with Esaias van de Velde. In 1617, de Neyn married in Leiden and
continued his career as a painter. His second line of business was stone cutting.

PIETER CLAESZ (1597 - Haarlem - 1661)

"A Richly laid table with two Berkemeyers and a Façon-de-Venise Wineglass on a Silver Dish, Olives in a Porcelain Dish, a Bread Roll, a Lemon Peel and a Slice of Lemon on a Pewter Plate, Sweetmeats in a tazza, a Pigeon Pie, a Silver-gilt Standing Cup and Cover, an overturned Silver Flagon, Nuts, a Knife, all on a Table partly draped with two White Linen Cloths"

"The Basket with Fruits and Sprays of Vines" by Roelof Koets (circa 1592/3 - Haarlem - 1655)
Oil on canvas: 136 x 206 cm; signed with monogram PC (on the bread dish) and remnants of a date 16.. (on the pewter plate); painted circa 1648-1650.

Provenance: a private collection of a family of Dutch descent living in Frankfurt, and kept in this family for many generations, until circa 1994, when it was sold to a private gentleman collector; sale London, Sotheby's, 6 July 1994, lot no.68; sale London, Sotheby's, 3-4 December 1997, lot no.68; Amsterdam, Gebr. Douwes Fine Art; from a private Belgian collection

Expertise: Sam Segal, Amsterdam 16 September 1988, as painted entirely by Pieter Claesz, circa 1650;

Literature: S. Segal, "Masters of the Monochrome Banquet Piece" (addendum to the exhibition catalogue 'A Prosperous Past'), 1988, fig.4; Martina Brunner-Bulst, "Pieter Claesz. der Hauptmeister des Haarlemer Stillebens im 17. Jahrhundert", Luca Verlag, Lingen, 2004, cat.no. 167 p. 300 with colour ill. on p. 97 and text on p. 182.

Exhibition: Leeuwarden, Fries Museum, 'Van Jan Steen tot Jan Sluijters, De smaak van Douwes', Nov. 1998 - Feb. 1999, ill. no.10; Haarlem, Frans Hals Museum - Kunsthaus Zürich, "Pieter Claesz, Meester van het stilleven in de Gouden Eeuw", Nov. 2004 - April 2005, cat.no.44, p. 106, with ill.

Notes: the right half of this still life was painted by Roelof Koets (fruits and foliage). Pieter Claesz and Roelof Koets worked together over the years in a total of ten paintings. In the years 1647/48, they worked together on two other paintings apart from this one (Brunner-Bulst p. 182). In its composition, the rich colours, the impasto brushwork, and the extraordinarily large size, this largest known painting by Claesz comes closest to a large painting in Berlin (BB cat. no 169).

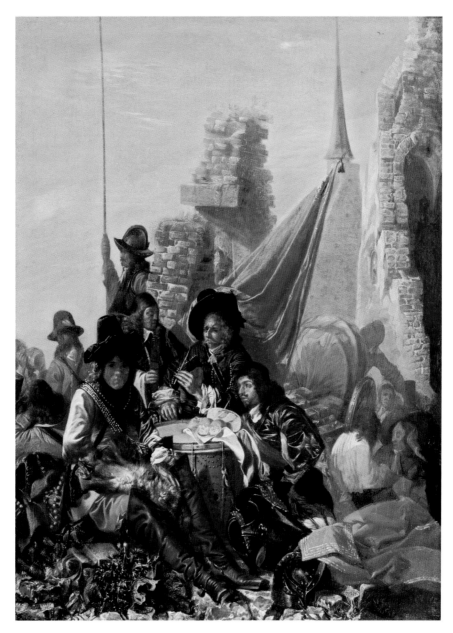

NICOLAES van GALEN (1620 - Hasselt, Belgium - 1683)
"Soldiers enjoying a Meal amidst the Ruins of a Dutch Town"
Oil on panel: 38,5 x 28,5 cm; fully signed and dated 1648 (l.r.)

Provenance: from a private Dutch collection
Notes: This painting is an extremely rare example of a signed work by the history painter Van Galen. His only other known painting, signed and dated 1657, is kept in Hasselt. For a brief period in about 1650, he was active in Kampen (Holland). He was influenced by Henrdrick Terbrugghen long after the demise of Caravaggism. In Hasselt, Van Galen is mentioned in 1676 as the head of the local Hospital, and in 1683 as the head of the local Pawn Bank ('Bank van Lening'). He painted mainly allegorical subjects and genre scenes.
This subject could well be a tribute to the end of the 'Eighty Year's War' between the Dutch and the Spanish in 1648.

JACOB van RUISDAEL (Haarlem 1628/29 - 1682 Amsterdam)
"Landscape with a Waterfall, Travellers and a Dog, a town beyond"
Oil on canvas: 55 x 63,5 cm; signed and dateable to the late 1660s, early 1670s.

Provenance: Herman de Kat, Dordrecht; his sale Paris, Drouot, 2 May 1866, no.70; Etienne le Roy (1808-1878), administrator of the Royal Museum of London (his seal on stretcher); sale Viscount de Buisseret, Brussels, 29 April 1891, no. 94 to Raoul Waroquier; F.J. Castellain, Notary in Seneffe (his seal on stretcher); Marquis d'Assche of Brussels; purchased from him by Jan de Boever's father in 1979; Jan de Boever, Paris, by 1979; private collection, Belgium.
Note: Jan de Boever kindly provided rubbings of the red lacquer stamps of Etienne le Roy, Brussels, and F. J. Castelain, a notary of Seneffe, Belgium, which are on the stretcher of the painting
Literature: Kunstkroniek, 18, 1857, p. 11; C. Hofstede de Groot, "A Catalogue Raisonné of the works of the most eminent Dutch Painters of the 17th Century", 1911, no. 415; Seymour Slive, "Jacob van Ruisdael, complete catalogue", New Haven & London, 2001, no.252, p. 223, with ill.
Notes: the chronology of Ruisdael's paintings of waterfalls is very hard to establish due to the paucity of dated works. Though he had certainly begun painting these subjects by the late 1650s, the present picture seems to have been painted a full decade later. While still displaying some of the characteristics of his heroic waterfalls of the 1650s, the quieter, more idyllic mood of the present landscape is typical of Ruisdael's paintings of the late 1660s and early 1670s.

JAQUES de CLAEUW (circa 1620 - Dordrecht - after 1689)
"Flower Still Life with Cherries and Oranges"
Oil on panel: 37 x 31 cm; fully signed and to be dated circa 1650.

Provenance: a Dutch private Estate until 1995; from a private collection.
Expertise: Dr. Sam Segal, Amsterdam, 27-9-1996
Exhibition: Leeuwarden, Fries Museum, 'Van Jan Steen tot Jan Sluijters, De smaak van Douwes', from Nov.1998 until Febr.1999.
Notes: He usually painted colourful flower still lifes against a dark background, with small insects and shells.
He was Jan van Goyen's son-in-law, and Jan Steen's brother-in-law.

JAN ABRAHAMZ. BEERSTRATEN (1622 – Amsterdam - 1666)
"A Dutch V.O.C. ship mooring at a Levant harbour, with a fortified tower to the left"
Oil on panel: 70 x 60 cm; signed with monogram (l.r. on the rock)

Provenance: an English private collection; bought by Douwes Fine Art in London, 1980's; art dealer Jacques van Rijn, Maastricht; a Belgian private collection; from a foreign collection.

Notes: He painted town views of Amsterdam, scenes of battles at sea, and busy harbours in southern Europe. Characteristic of his work are the harmonious tonalities of his choice of colours. In 1642, he married for the first time and had five children. In 1665, as a widower, he became engaged once again, but died a year later at the age of forty-four.

ESAIAS van de VELDE (Amsterdam 1587 - 1630 The Hague)
"A River View with boats and travellers"
Black chalk: 18,5 x 30 cm; signed with monogram VE (l.l.)

Provenance: Gebr. Douwes Fine Art, Amsterdam, 1970's; from a private Dutch collection.
Notes: He probably received his earliest training from the Antwerp painter Gilles van Coninxloo, who moved to Amsterdam in 1595, or David Vinckboons. In 1612 he became a member of the Haarlem Guild of St. Luke, the same year as Willem Buytewech and Hercules Seghers. By 1618, he had moved to The Hague.

JAN van GOYEN (Leiden 1596 - 1656 The Hague)
"Landscape with cows, hay fields and a windmill"
Black chalk and wash: 11,5 x 18,5 cm; signed with monogram VG and dated 1652.

Provenance: Fred. Muller & Co, Amsterdam, 1906; Gebr. Douwes Fine Art, Amsterdam, 1980; from a private Dutch collection
Literature: H-U. Beck "Jan van Goyen", 1972, no.292. *Exhibition*: Douwes Fine Art, Amsterdam, 1981, no.30

ROELANT SAVERY (Courtrai 1576 - 1639 Utrecht)
"A mountainous Landscape with Travellers near a Village"
Red chalk, pen and brown ink, and watercolour: 25,3 x 40,2 cm;
on paper with a watermark: Castle with the letter 'N' (1603); signed with monogram.

Literature: Dr. Joaneath Spicer (by letter of October 2000) will include the drawing in her forthcoming oeuvre catalogue as by Roelant Savery, done "at the beginning of Saverij's sojourn in Prague, circa 1603-1604.The style and subject matter are consistent with other drawings attributable to this period, as is the watermark."

Notes: He was the brother of Hans Savery (1564-1585) and Jacob Savery (1565-1603), both painters in their own right. In 1580, Roelant accompanies his father to Bruges. In 1585, they both went to Haarlem, and in 1591 to Amsterdam. Some time before 1602, he became the pupil of his brother Jacob Savery. In 1604, he went to Prague and was appointed court painter to Emperor Rudolf II, and later to Emperor Mathias. In the next ten years, he made visits to Tyrol, Salzburg, and Munich. In 1618, he was recorded as being in Haarlem, and a year later in Utrecht. One of his pupils was Allart van Everdingen, and he collaborated with painters such as Cornelis Poelenburgh, Jacob Pynas, Joachim Wtewael, Cornelis van Haarlem and Gillis d'Hondecoeter.

HIERONUMUS van der MIJ (1687 - Leiden - 1761)
"Homely Scene with a Mother nourishing her Baby"
Oil on panel: 37 x 32,5 cm; bears signature "W v. Mieris"

Provenance: from the collection of the aristocratic Bentinck family, owners of the 17th century Castle Weldam, The Netherlands;
a private collection in Munich; from a private German collection, since the 1970s.
Expertise: Dr. Walter Bernt, Munich.
Notes: As is often the case with his paintings, this panel bears the signature of Willem van Mieris, his teacher, whose reputation exceeded his own at the time. Van der Mij seems to have been an art dealer, and a designer of garden vases. In 1736, he and Frans van Mieris the Younger continued as directors of the Leiden art academy, taking over from the founders Willem van Mieris and Carel de Moor.

A Synopsis of art historical Notes

We do hope that these notes will give you a better insight into the five centuries of the history of painting and art dealing. This text has been compiled by us and is frequently used during the many talks and slide shows our firm organises for any interested parties.

"A collector misses the point of collecting if he knows the price of everything, but the value of nothing"

The decline and fall of Antwerp

As early as 1460, out of Antwerp's 100,000 citizens not even 20 were professional painters and accounted for, whereas by 1560, as many as 300 master painters (official members of the St. Lucas Guild) had set up independent workshops. In comparison to today's society, it seems difficult to believe that, at the same time, there were only 170 bakers and 80 butchers in this prosperous city.

The Antwerp painters developed a broad scale of new artistic genres and themes mirroring the social and religious patterns of those days. After the decline and subsequent fall of Antwerp to the Spanish in 1585, however, many of the enterprising merchants and skilled craftsmen fled from Flanders to the newly formed United Dutch Provinces. They were to have a powerful impact on the social and economic life in the North.

The 'Golden Age' in Dutch History

Amsterdam in the 16th century counted fewer inhabitants than Leiden or Utrecht, but by the beginning of the 17th century this northern city profited tremendously from the political changes in the South. While Antwerp's population declined from 100,000 to less than 50,000, the Amsterdam population grew from 30,000 to over 100,000, within one generation. Many Flemish painters settled in Middelburg, Haarlem, and Amsterdam. An excellent example of their influence in the northern provinces was the Flemish painter, Adriaen Brouwer, who worked in Haarlem between 1625 and 1631. With his Pieter Brueghel style of painting, he stimulated genre painting with interior scenes showing the life of cheerful country folk, later followed by the exceptional Adriaen van Ostade (1610–1685), who was to excel in this genre.

Eager to discover new worlds and exercising their political freedom, the Dutch developed a lively trade overseas, which led to extraordinary wealth. For over four generations, there was no holding back from what we now so aptly call 'the Golden Age' in Dutch history. Originally, most of this wealth came from the world's first real 'limited' company, the *Verenigde Oostindische Compagnie - V.O.C.* ('United East Indian Company'), established in 1602. For that period, it is extraordinary to know that in six months 35,000 shareholders subscribed to a total of 6,500,000 florins in capital stock. The Amsterdam share alone amounted to 50% of that total, which is over US$ 325,000,000 at today's rate. The buying power of the 'Carolingian' florin can today be valued at US$ 50. A solid banking system was introduced, and the Stock Exchange building opened in Amsterdam in 1611. In that same year, the V.O.C. paid out an extra dividend over the previous nine years of a staggering 175%, partly in cash, stocks, and in 'kind', such as the spices imported from overseas. The rise of the Dutch Republic was paid for from its trade profits. And the first limited company 'V.O.C.' can equally be seen as one of the world's first 'multinationals'.

The Guilds

Holland was a country effectively made up of cities. They did not nurture a culture of aristocracy, and the influence of the Church levelled out considerably after the decline of the Reformation. It was the cities' middle class that mainly supported the social and economic daily life. This implied a broadly based wealth; there was hardly any elitism. The Protestant religion preached in favour of soberness and against waste. This simple yet strict Calvinistic feeling explains, to a great extent, the cautiousness and sobriety of the Dutch character.

The St. Lucas Guild was first constituted in France in 1391. Tradition says that the evangelist Saint Luke once painted the Virgin Mary, and was therefore nominated to become the patron saint of the arts and crafts.
To the various professions of this guild also belonged the glass-blowers, sign-writers, guilders and bronzers, restorers, book publishers, artisans and painters, art dealers, and the like.
Already in the Middle Ages, there were two groups of organized craftsmen. A so-called society of building contractors and architects, the Freemasons, who would have to adhere religiously to what their, mostly clerical, commissioners demanded. The other group were the organized guilds, with independent members. These members exercised free choice over their artistic output, while the guilds would guard the technical outlines and assist with any business disputes. They proposed schooling for students who wanted to become painters and establish their own studios. There was quality control on products, such as paints, linen, and panels, and they stimulated the general well being of their members.

Paintings as an investment

Painters cultivated the taste of the 'burgher', who did not want dramatic large canvasses at home, but rather 'a joy to their eyes'. They wanted to have value for money. Originally, the price of a traditional work was calculated to the cost of the materials and the working hours of the artists involved. No wonder that many painters needed additional resources to keep their, usually large, families afloat. As an example, we can mention Jan Steen (1626–1679), who ran a pub in Leiden or Jan van de Capelle (1624-1679), who was a textile merchant. Furthermore, there were Willem Kalf (1622-1693), who became an antique dealer, Jacob van Ruysdael (1628–1682), who was a surgeon, and Jan van der Heijden (1637-1712), who bought patents on inventions. It was just a matter of time before the society's prestige, its popularity and the use of paintings as a temporary loan, inflated the prices for works of art. We should not underestimate the importance during the 17th century of paintings as an investment. There was a lively art market, with a healthy competition.

The reason for the large quantities of paintings on offer at f.i. the so-called 'free-markets', was the amazing fact that inhabitants were faced with a shortage of land to invest in. When the Englishman John Evelyn visited Rotterdam in 1641 he recorded in his diaries: 'It was, therefore, common practice to see a simple Dutch farmer spend 2,000 to 3,000 Pounds for these paintings'. The seascape painter Simon de Vlieger paid for his house in paintings, each costing close to 16 guilders. A painting by Gerard Dou on the other hand, made between 600 and 1000 guilders, and this was enough to buy him a house in the city.

In a flourishing economy, a free art market has always blossomed. The unparalleled growth, and distinctly bourgeois and realistic character of Dutch art were a direct result of the great economic prosperity of the predominantly protestant United Provinces, once they had gained autonomy from Spain.
The idea behind the concept of an 'economy' reappeared in Florence around 1,000 AD. Money was given in

custody to banks, which, in turn, earned well on loans. For centuries, the famous Medici banking family was the largest commissioner of art.

During the Middle Ages, the Catholic Church regarded borrowing against interest more or less as a sin, because Aristotle (384 B.C.-322 B.C.) had reasoned that money is sterile and rigid, therefore, could not produce by itself. In practice, this meant that the middle class in catholic countries did not stand much of a chance to expand their economies, because they were dependent on trade, with the implication of 'risk capital'. In the northern countries, however, the intellectual spokesman Calvin (1509-1564) argued that earning money was a moral duty, and making a profit a goal in itself. But he felt that only strict soberness and discipline would finally lead to God. The German 'politician' Luther (1483-1546), extended this belief by adding extra value to the term 'profession' with an emphasis on 'vocation'. Thus a person lived religiously by fulfilling his worldly tasks and duties, while underwriting modern capitalistic ethics.

The Calvinist doctrine condemned the worship of religious images and their display in churches, and mainly for this reason portraiture, genre painting, landscape, and still life became favourite subjects of the middle class. 'Painting' had to be able to demonstrate by itself the desirability of what money could buy.

Painting as a living

The painter, Rubens (1577-1640), one of the most gifted and famous painters of our times, received a daily income of one hundred florins, which comes to a present rate of over US $ 5,000 per day. At one time, the well-known painter David Teniers (1582–1649) had a most productive workshop with 36 pupils. Such a pupil, already a skilled painter at a tender age, had permission to sell a few of his own works per annum in order to provide for his tuition fee. As a matter of simple 'quality control', pupils would have to obtain the master's signature on their paintings, before they left Teniers's workshop. This practice was common amongst master painters, and inadvertently caused authenticity problems for experts and art historians of later generations in the course of their researches. During the education with a master painter, apprentices were encouraged to 'copy' works and improve their skills by practicing. In the ethics of their craftsmanship, these copies were not seen as 'forgeries'. It may also be significant to learn that during the 17th century the average trade price of a copy was half that of an original. Therefore, it seemed much less complicated to adjust to the taste and fashion of the day by copying two saleable replicas than to create a new work of art.

The painter, Jan van Goyen (1596–1656), on the other hand, had more difficulty selling his own 'free-style' work, and resorted to other means of income such as speculating in tulip bulbs. They ran into large sums of twenty and thirty florins a piece. Later though, at the height of the so-called 'tulip mania' in 1636-1637, one exceptional tulip bulb could be exchanged for a whole farmstead including its livestock. Van Goyen was fortunate enough to be able to fall back on working in his wife's family inn. For many years, he was not able to buy natural colours to mix on his palette, which accounted for his well-known brownish landscapes. His widow was finally left behind with a burden of debts of up to 18,000 florins (at today's rate: US$ 900,000), and only after all of her belongings had been sold, could she pay off her debts and was left with 270 florins. She died a month later.

Various influences

In the 18th century, the aftermath of the Golden Age, a gradual waning of creativity and a comfortable thriving on the established riches followed. It was also the time that auction sales became popular. And it was dealer/painter

Gerard Hoet (1648-1733), an art critic and publisher of art books, who was the first to edit printed sales catalogues of past and present auctions with full details, descriptions, and prices. Many Museums were founded during this century, and their collections grew with works of contemporary artists. This may also explain why it is difficult to find excellent examples by important masters, such as Cornelis Troost, Jan van Huysem, Jan Ekels, and others.

During the late 18th century, the many excavations in Italy prompted steady visits by artists to the 'Old Rome'. This, in turn, led to a change of artistic power and showed a revival of many different styles of art, especially in France and England. In France, of course, Napoleon put his stamp on the arts of around 1800, and favoured Classicism with painters such as Jean-Louis David (1748-1825), who idolized the Emperor's triumphs.
The influence of the Art Academies was strongly felt. An important but unorthodox painter such as Eugene Delacroix (1798-1863) was only admitted to the Academy just before he died, and his critical comment speaks loudly for itself: "Beauty in art is being taught as if it is plain mathematics". After the French Revolution in 1789, the social structures changed dramatically, from the declining nobility to the more critical and free working classes.

After Napoleon's defeat in 1815, the Dutch painters distanced themselves from France, and looked more towards the East, such as Germany and Italy. In Holland, most academies for the arts were set up during this generation. Meanwhile, Louis Napoleon abolished the Guilds in 1808. And today, Douwes Fine Art is the only existing art gallery and restoration studio that was a member of the St.Lucas Guild before 1808.

One of the important influences of the 19th century Romantic and realistic feelings in painting comes from English artists such as Thomas Gainsborough (1727-1788), John Constable (1776-1837), William Turner (1775-1851), and Richard Bonnington (1801-1828). They travelled widely in France and Italy, and during one of the earlier Salon exhibitions in Paris in 1824, they were the inspiration of many young French painters. Their motto was: 'paint everything outdoors as you experience it, not as you would wish it to be'. The mood of nature, and the insignificance of man became a source of inspiration: the German painter Caspar David Friedrich (1774–1840) translated Beethoven's ode to nature, his sixth symphony, into a painting. It became one of his famous documents depicting a lonely person overlooking this vast and mountainous landscape.

Under the influence of inventions such as the steam engine, the first forms of direct communication, the railway and the steamboat, the countries' economies and their art world changed rapidly. After the final division of the Northern and Southern parts of the Netherlands into Holland and Belgium in 1830, King William III stimulated the Arts by publicly starting collecting, and by introducing scholarships for painters to develop their skills abroad. A painter like Jongkind benefitted from this opportunity.
About 1850, artists were seeking reality and political liberalism, gaining self-confidence and positivism in their work.
In this context, many French painters studied the realism and directness of Dutch 17th century landscape paintings, such as the work of Ruysdael (1628–1682) and Hobbema (1638–1709). And from 1848, a group of landscape painters settled in the small village of Barbizon, south of Paris. Amongst them were Théodore Rousseau, Constant Troyon, Jules Dupré, Charles Daubigny, Jean-François Millet, and Charles Jacque.. It was their intention to paint nature 'realistically', often with loose brushwork and lots of atmosphere, resulting in 'plein-air' painting. Also, the delicate works of Camille Corot (1796-1875) should be mentioned in this context.

The social change of the working classes demanded more quality of life, and equality. Painters such as Gustave Courbet (1819-1877) and Honore Daumier (1808-1879) represented their views in art.

Around 1860, Courbet, Boudin (1824-1898), Jongkind (1819-1891), and Monet (1840-1926) met in the coastal village of Honfleur, in the local and renowned Inn of Saint Simeon. Soon after, these contacts and artistic exchanges led to the new style of Impressionism. Of course, with a little help from someone like Edouard Manet (1832-1883), whose painting 'Dejeuner sur l'herbe' caused a scandal in 1863.

In about 1874, an art critic dubbed it 'impressionism', after having seen Monet's 'l'Impression levant au Soleil'. The colours were not mixed on the palette, but in pure form painted next to each other onto the canvas, which 'trembles from liveliness and light', almost like the immediate moment of a photograph just taken. In contrast, expressionism, with pioneers such as our countryman Vincent van Gogh (1853-1890), did not use their 'eyes' so much as their 'soul'!

Already as early as 1882, Isaac Israels (1865-1934), at the tender age of 17, was greeted at the French Salon as the Dutch exponent of Impressionism, whereas Georg Hendrik Breitner (1857-1923) was seen as the inspiring pioneer of the 'new movement' in Holland. With his strong temperament, he distanced himself from just 'beauty' and preferred realism in earthly colours.

Parallel to painting, the strong development in literature was impossible to stop. This in turn would help painters with their manifests in giving more depth to works of art by justifying and expressing the social and political changes in society.

In Holland, Jan Toorop (1858-1928) translated the spiritual and social feelings of Dutch society into an almost religious symbolism. Linear forms give a renewed meaning and supersede the photographic images.

Throughout Europe, breaking through to the new 'isms' of the 20th century meant a leap from the visual world to the 'spiritual world': 'from cover to content'. 'L'Art pour l'art' – art for art's sake – is fading away now. Producing art with "a message" became the new direction.

Stadhouderskade & Museumhotel, c. 1888

Painting by Carel Willink:
'The Zeppelin', 1933

Douwes Fine Art, Amsterdam, 2002

"The old-fashioned, conscientious fine art dealer is at heart a fanatical collector."

FRANCINA LOUISE SCHOT (Rotterdam 1816 - 1894 Schaarbeek, Brussels)
"An extensive bouquet of Flowers in a Delft Vase, various Fruits and a Pumpkin on a carved Table"
Oil on panel: 68 x 59 cm; signed and dated 1846 (l.r.)

Provenance: an American collection; from a Belgian private collection
Exhibition: Leeuwarden, Fries Museum, 'Van Jan Steen tot Jan Sluijters, De smaak van Douwes', Nov. 1998-Feb.1999, in cat.
Notes: She was an accomplished painter of still lifes, and started her career in Rotterdam. In 1847, she became a member of the Royal Academy of Art in Amsterdam. Later, in 1882, she worked in The Hague, and in 1885 left for Jumet, Belgium. After the death of her husband P.H.Martin, she moved to Schaarbeek in 1891.

PETER PAUL JOSEPH NOËL (Waulsort-sur-Meuse 1789 - 1822 Sosoye, Namur)
"The Prinsengracht in Amsterdam with a view of the Westertoren on the far right,
in the left foreground a boat loaded with vegetables, and lively Townfolk"
Oil on panel: 49,5 x 71 cm; signed and dated 1813 (l.r.)

Provenance: from a private collection.
Notes: In early 1800, he studied at the Antwerp art academy, worked in Brussels, and in 1814 was a pupil of J. Swebach in Paris. From 1820,
Noël worked in Holland and visited England. In his work, he developed a preference for romantic landscapes with people,
and anecdotal genre scenes in the Dutch tradition.

ANDRIES SCHELFHOUT (1787 - The Hague - 1870)
"A Frozen River with Wood Gatherers at the end of the Day"
Oil on panel: 38,5 x 50 cm; signed and dated 1845 (l.l.)

Provenance: collection A.A.C. de Vries Robbé, Gorinchem, 1930-2002.
Literature: W. Laanstra, "Andreas Schelfhout 1787-1870", Amsterdam 1995, cat.no. W 1845-3, p.85, with ill.
Exhibition: Ede, Simonis & Buunk Gallery, 'Onsterfelijk Schoon. De landschappen van Andreas Schelfhout (1787-1870) en zijn leerlingen',
27 Jan.-13 March 2005, illustrated on page 16.
Notes: In the 1840s, Schelfhout's *'winters'* were greatly admired, even to the extent that art critics called him the 'Claude Lorrain of the winter landscapes'. But in contrast to the French Lorrain (1600-1682), who idealised his pastoral landscapes with an atmospheric morning or evening light, Schelfhout based his work on the reality and recognisability of the Dutch wintry atmosphere and landscape.

WILLEM JOSEPH LAQUY (Brühl 1738 - 1798 Kleef)
"A busy Household of an elegant Family around a Table eating Waffles, with Maids Cooking and Serving"
Oil on panel: 58,5 x 50,5 cm; signed and dated 1775.

Provenance: an American private collection; from a private Dutch collection in Belgium.
Notes: He soon came to Amsterdam and joined the wallpaper factory of J. Remmers. Painted the staffage in works by W. Hendriks.
He made drawings of the old master paintings in the Braamkamp collection. His oeuvre consisted of portraiture and genre scenes.

GERALDINE JACOBA van de SANDE BAKHUYZEN (1826 - The Hague - 1895)
"Handpicked Flowers on a Forest floor"
Oil on panel: 26,5 x 36 cm; signed and dated 1858 (l.r.); old collection number on the verso: '36'.

Provenance: from a private Dutch collection.
Notes: She was an accomplished painter of fruit and flower still lifes. In her early career, she also painted landscapes.
Geraldine was a pupil of her father Hendrikus van de Sande Bakhuyzen.

BAREND CORNELIS KOEKKOEK (Middelburg 1803 - 1862 Kleef)
*"A Hilly Landscape with Travellers on the Road to Cleve, in the distance is the Mediaeval Schwanenburg
and the Kapittel church"*
Oil on panel: 29,5 x 40 cm; signed with monogram and dated 1854;
on verso there is a statement of authenticity sealed by the artist, and dated 1854

Provenance: Gebr. Douwes Fine Art in Amsterdam, circa 1990's; from a private Dutch collection.
Notes: This second generation Barend Koekkoek, when painting this landscape in 1854, was at the pinnacle of his fame.
He can undoubtedly be considered the most important exponent of the 19th century Dutch Romantic School. His influence on a large group
of painters was enormous, and in 1841 resulted in the founding of a drawing academy: the so-called "Zeichen-Collegium", in Cleve.

WILLEM GRUYTER Junior (1817 - Amsterdam - 1880)
"A Paddleboat on the River Merwede near Dordrecht"
Oil on canvas: 81,5 x 130 cm; signed and dated 1875.

Provenance: from the C.W. van Blijenburg collection, 1990's.
Notes: He was a pupil of Hermanus Koekkoek, and painted mainly river scenes and seascapes with lots of ships. In 1845, he joined the Royal Academy of Art in Amsterdam, and in 1853 became a member of 'Arti et Amicitiae' (a society for visual artists in Amsterdam).

CORNELIS SPRINGER (Amsterdam 1817 - 1891 Hilversum)
"View of Enkhuizen, behind the Vissersdijk"
Oil on panel: 31 x 41,5 cm; signed and dated '75 (l.r.);
on verso: with a statement of authenticity, signed by the artist, and dated 1 January 1878.

Provenance: P.L.F. Kluijver, who bought it directly from the artist in 1875; coll. Mrs de Vries-Bleek, Canada; sale Sotheby's Mak van Waay, Amsterdam, April 1978, lot no.223; from a private Dutch collection.
Literature: W. Laanstra, H.C. de Bruijn and Dr.J.H.A. Ringeling, "Cornelis Springer (1817-1891)", Tableau, Utrecht 1984, no.75-II.
Notes: He became a student of the art academy in Amsterdam, in 1827. Later, until 1835, he was taught by J. van der Stok and Herman G. ten Cate. Between 1835-1837, Springer joined Kaspar Karsen. In 1847, as a member of the association 'Felix Meritis' in Amsterdam, he received a gold medal for a Church interior. Together with Jozef Israels, he was invited in 1878 by the Interior Ministry to give his views on the plans for the founding of the Rijksmuseum. Amongst his students were Adrianus Eversen, J.C. Greive, and J.A.Rust.

HENRIËTTE RONNER-KNIP (Amsterdam 1821 - 1909 Brussels)
"Two Kittens on a Table, one small kitten sniffing at a Glass Jug, and a glass cover for Cheese"
Oil on panel, maroufflé: 25 x 37 cm; fully signed.

Provenance: sale Amsterdam, Mak van Waay, 8 March 1961, no 632; from a private Dutch collection
Notes: She was a pupil of her father Joseph A. Knip, and lived near Den Bosch. Married to Teico Ronner in 1850, she moved to Brussels.
She painted landschap and animal scenes. From 1870 onwards, her interest shifted to the depiction of cats in all their different moods and poses.

BERNARD de HOOG (1866 - Amsterdam - 1943)
"A Pleasant Family Day in the Dunes"
Oil on canvas: 40,5 x 50 cm; fully signed (l.r.)

Provenance: from a Dutch private collection
Notes: He lived and worked in Amsterdam until 1899, next in Laren until 1902, in Haarlem in 1903, and subsequently in Bussum until 1924.
During the last twenty years of his productive life, he worked in The Hague. De Hoog specialized in sunny landscapes and farm interiors, which
connects him chiefly with the 'Laren' School of painting. Many of his paintings were 'exported' to England, Canada and the United States.

WILLEM KOEKKOEK (Amsterdam 1839 - 1895 Nieuwer-Amstel)
"A sunny Town view with locals strolling along a winding Street leading to a Drawbridge"
Oil on canvas: 45 x 59,5 cm; fully signed.

Provenance: from a private Dutch collection.

Notes: The Koekkoek family consisted of five generations of painters, who practically all were active during the 19th century. Willem belongs to the third generation, and became a pupil of his father Hermanus (brother of Barend Cornelis). Before 1878, he worked in The Hague, and until 1888 in Amsterdam, and in the small nearby village of Nieuwer-Amstel. The final years of his life, he lived and worked in London. His specialty were the lively and colourful town views crowded with figures, with scenes set in both summer and winter.

ISAAC ISRAELS (Amsterdam 1865 - 1934 The Hague)
"The Boxing lesson"
Oil on canvas: 60 x 50,5 cm; signed (l.r.)

Exhibited: Los Angeles Museum of History, Science and Art, "The X-th Olympiad", 1932.
Notes From 1912 to 1948, art competitions were held at the Olympic Games. The idea for these competitions came from Pierre de Frédy, Baron de Coubertin, founder of the modern Olympic Movement. Medals were awarded in five areas: architecture, literature, music, painting, and sculpture, to works of art inspired by sport.Because of the economic situation and the remote location of Los Angeles, participation in the athletic events of the 1932 Games was lower than in those of 1928. However, the art competition did not suffer from it, and the number of art works entered remained stable. Their exhibition drew 384.000 visitors to the Los Angeles Museum of History, Science and Art.
Isaac Israels is one of only a few important Dutch Impressionist painters. He was the son of the Hague School painter Jozef Israels, and studied at the art academies of The Hague (1880-1882) and Amsterdam (1886-1887). He is also known for his exquisite watercolours. His favourite subjects were equestrian scenes, town views and parks with elegant women and children, beach scenes with happy families, or donkey riding. Between 1871 and 1903, Israels worked and lived in The Hague and Amsterdam, stayed in Paris between 1904 and 1913, next in London for one year, and back in The Hague from 1920 on. Meanwhile, he also travelled to Switzerland, the Dutch East Indies (1921), and Italy (1925).

JOHANNES CRISTIAAN KAREL KLINKENBERG (1852 - The Hague - 1924)
"The Amstel River in Amsterdam, with a view towards the 'Magere Brug' (the famous Drawbridge), to the left the Carré theatre, and the Amstel Hotel beyond"
Oil on canvas: 58 x 76 cm; signed and dated 1921.

Provenance: J.H. van Heek, 's Heerenberg; Sotheby's, Amsterdam, November 1960; from a private Dutch collection.
Literature: W. Laanstra, "Johannes Christiaan Karel Klinkenberg 1852 - 1924, de meester van het zonnige stadsgezicht", Laren 2000, cat. no. O/58-3, p. 178 with illustration.
Notes: Among others, he was a pupil of Cornelis Bisschop, and started by painting landscapes and history scenes. It was not until after the 1880's that Klinkenberg focussed more on his famous city views, bathing in an abundance of sunlight. He was an accomplished watercolourist, as well. During his impressive career, he received many medals and prizes for his work, such as gold medals in Amsterdam, Munich, and Paris. He was awarded distinguished titles in Saxen-Weimar, Bayern, and Belgium, and was decorated an Officer in the Order of Orange-Nassau in the Netherlands in 1909.

CHARLES FRANÇOIS DAUBIGNY (1817 - Paris - 1878)
"Le pont de Meulan"
Oil on panel: 43,5 x 82 cm; signed and dated 1865.

Provenance: collection A. Young; Agnew & Co. in London; Van Wisselingh, Amsterdam; from a private Dutch collection since the 1960's.
Literature: Fidell-Beaufort, Bailly & Herzberg: "Daubigny, la vie et l'oeuvre", Paris, 1975; cat.no.87, with ill. on p. 156; Robert Hellebranth, "Charles-François Daubigny", Morges 1976, cat.no.59 (Hellebranth has confused the illustrations of no.59 and our no.60).

"La Seine vers Portejoie"
Oil on panel: 39 x 67,5 cm; signed and dated 1877.

Provenance: Daubigny sale no.442; David Warfield, New York; Jacob H.Schiff, New York; Walter Craig, New York; Schweitzer Gallery; private Dutch collection; private collection in Belgium.
Literature: R. Hellebranth, "Charles-François Daubigny", Morges 1976, no.114, p.42 with ill.
Exhibition: Maastricht, Jacques van Rijn, 'Haagse School en Barbizon', 1984
Notes: He was born in Paris into a family of painters. In 1836, he went on foot to Italy and, upon his return, worked as a restorer of paintings in the Musée du Louvre. In 1843, he made his first of many visits to the forest of Fontainebleau, advocating 'plein-air' painting. Courbet was his prime influence, and Corot his faithful friend and critic. With the latter, he travelled to Switzerland in 1852. Daubigny's devotion to river landscapes, with its seasonal changes and reflections, was evident after 1857, when he travelled extensively along the Seine and Oise, in his specially constructed 'Bottin' (the Little Box). Besides being the most important and modern exponent of the Barbizon School, he also paved the way for Impressionism and became a direct influence on Claude Monet, from whom he bought a painting in 1872.

NARCISSE VIRGILE DIAZ de la PEÑA (Bordeaux 1807 - 1876 Menton)
"Nymphs and Cupids, in an extensive landscape"
Oil on canvas: 57 x 47 cm; signed and dated '54 (l.l.)

Provenance: P. Cornette de Saint-Cyr, Espace Drouot, Paris, Nov. 1987, cat.no.21; Christie's New York, May 2001; from a private German collection.
Expertise: Pierre Miquel will include this work in his forthcoming catalogue raisonné (no. 2898)
Exhibition: Paris, Le Pavillon des Arts, "Diaz de la Peña", 1968.
Notes: Born of Spanish refugees, one-legged Narcisse Diaz was trained as a porcelain painter at Sèvres in 1823, where he met Jules Dupré and became his lifelong friend. Diaz had a love for landscape, combined with social portrayals of people. His first Salon contribution was in 1831, and as early as 1836 he visited Fontainebleau and became one of the leading figures of the Ecole de Barbizon.
The Barbizon School was a group of landscape artists working in the area of the French village of Barbizon, south of Paris. They rejected the Academic tradition and abandoned its theory in an attempt to achieve a truer representation of the countryside. This is why they painted outside rather than in a studio, advocating 'plein-air' painting. Diaz met Rousseau in 1837, and by 1843 he had met his fellow painters Troyon, Jacque, Millet, and Corot. His paintings are done in a very personal technique, which can be described as 'iridescent floating dabs of colour'. The Impressionists, and even Van Gogh were much inspired by his fanciful and empirical naturalism, providing surfaces of rich and varied lights.

JOSEPH BAIL (Limonest 1862 - 1921 Paris)
"Interior with two Maids folding the Linen"
Oil on canvas: 55 x 46 cm; fully signed.

Provenance: from the Pommery Champagne family.
Notes: As the youngest son of the painter Jean Antoine Bail (1830-1919), Joseph Bail was introduced to the artistic Romantic heritage that characterized painting in Lyon, as well as to the development of Realist art he observed in the canvases of his father. He received training from Jean L. Gérôme and Carolus-Duran. Among his popular compositions are a series of cooks preparing food, cleaning utensils, smoking, playing cards, suggesting that Bail was familiar with the work of Chardin and Théodule Ribot. His works show a subtle knowledge of light, for he often placed figures in silhouette against a brilliant light source. The middle class found his work attractive and appealing, and he had much success at the various Salon exhibitions, where, between the 1880's and early 1900's, he was awarded numerous prizes.
In 1902, he received a medal of honour at the Salon for his continued dedication to the Realist aesthetics, at a time when newer styles of painting were capturing the allegiance of younger painters.

JEAN FRANÇOIS RAFFAËLLI (1850 – Paris - 1924)
"Bouquet de Fleurs lumineaux"
Oil on canvas: 75 x 63 cm; fully signed (l.r.)

Provenance: from a French collection.

For comparison: This type of still life, mostly composed of an impasto painted bouquet of flowers in a glass vase, against a white background, and on a loosely draped tablecloth, is similar to one in the collection of the national Museum Kröller-Müller and the beautiful example, illustrated in the catalogue of 'A Feast of Colour' exhibition in the Noordbrabants Museum, Den Bosch, 1990, no.65, p.174.

Notes: Raffaëlli was also a sculptor and printmaker. After his interest in music and theatre, he turned to painting in 1870. Raffaëlli's career as a realist artist was launched with the support of various art critics. Later, the Impressionists influenced him, and, at the insistence of Edgar Degas, he was included in their group shows of 1880 and 1881. He became an important interpreter of suburban life during the Parisian expansion period. In his quest for Realism, he regarded e.g. the rag picker as a symbol of alienated individualism in modern industrial society. This led him to articulate a theory of realism that he christened 'caractérisme'. This celebrated and talented artist created for himself a new system of brush strokes in a 'whiskery' manner, which lends a fleeting impression of vividness to his colourful works, often resulting in a true feast of colours.

CLAUDE-EMILE SCHUFFENECKER (1851 - Paris - 1934)
"La jeune Femme bretonne"
Pastel : 46 x 30,5 cm; stamped with ES lotus monogram (l.l.), and circa 1886.

Provenance: collection Mme. Jeanne Schuffenecker (the artist's daughter); Hirschl & Adler Galleries, New York, June 1958; presented to Abraham M. Adler, New York City; private collection, San Francisco, USA.
Expertise and Literature: this pastel is accompanied by a certificate of authencity from Jill-Elyse Grossvogel and will be included in Volume II of the Claude-Emile Schuffenecker catalogue raisonné. Similar compositions: Jill-Elyse Grossvogel, Vol. I: CR295 and CR296; René Porro, "Claude-Emile Schuffenecker, Une Oeuvre melodieuse", 1992, p.213, drawing no.280.
Exhibitions: New York, Hirschl & Adler Galleries, "Emile Schuffenecker", Nov.- Dec. 1958, no.31 (illustrated with another image)
Notes: this work is one of a series of studies for the finished version of approximately the same size (CR297), first shown at the important 1958 Hirschl & Adler Schuffenecker exhibition organized by the artist's daughter Jeanne, as the first showing of her father's work in the USA. What is not visible in this preliminary version is the branch the young girl is holding in her left hand. This work was made during the summer visit of the artist to Concarneau in1886, only a few kilometres away from Pont-Aven. It was during this short stay, drawing and painting in this ancient walled city, that he met Emile Bernard.

JOHAN BARTHOLD JONGKIND (Lattrop 1819 - 1891 La-Côte-St.André)
"Petit Port sur la Meuse auprès Rotterdam"
Oil on canvas: 34,5 x 47 cm; signed and dated 'Jongkind 1883' (l.r.) and titled on the stretcher.

Provenance: various inventory numbers, possibly also from Durand-Ruel; Ch. Viguier, Paris; collection R.E. Duin, Rotterdam; from a private Dutch collection.
Literature: Adolphe Stein, Brame & Lorenceau, 'Jongkind, catalogue critique de l'oeuvre, Peinture I', Paris, 2003, cat. no. 839, ill.
Exhibitions: 1940, Amsterdam, E.J. van Wisselingh & Co., Exposition de peinture française no. 25; 1960, Van Wisselingh, no. 36; old label on verso: Gemeentemuseum The Hague 'Jongkind'.
Notes: It was not until Jongkind was 18 years old that he was finally able to go to The Hague on a scholarship, to study under Andreas Schelfhout (1787-1870). With a grant from the future King William III in 1846, he next moved to Paris. There, the realistic approach to nature, expressed by Constable, the Barbizon School, and his teacher Eugène Isabey, suited Jongkind perfectly. After the death of his beloved mother in August of 1854, a period of deep depression ensued. In November 1855, he left Paris abruptly for Rotterdam, for the next five years just remaining in Holland. His friend and art dealer 'Père' Martin kept him going by occasionally selling the canvases he continued sending to Paris. Such was his influence among his French colleagues that they voluntarily organised an auction, consisting entirely of their own works, to collect enough financial support for Jongkind to get him to return to Paris. And, after his five-year Dutch interval, he did finally settle in France in 1860, and became acquainted with Josephine Fesser. She became his pupil, and shared her family life with him till his death in 1891. Early impressionists such as Monet and Sisley were much indebted to Jongkind's characteristic fervour, not least his watercolour-technique with which he excelled in luminous expressiveness. Jongkind, who was almost six and a half feet tall, had the habit of wearing a top hat, which of course added to his formidable appearance.

MAURICE DE VLAMINCK (1876 - Paris - 1958)
"Une Vase de Fleurs avec Anse"
Oil on canvas: 61 x 46 cm; signed lower left: *Vlaminck.*

Provenance: Mme Boas, Paris (acquired directly from the artist); Galerie de l'Elysee (Axel Maguy), Paris; a private collection; sale New York (Christie's), 12 Nov. 1997, no.418, ill.; from a private collection, England

Literature: To be included in the forthcoming monograph with *catalogue raisonné* of de Vlaminck's work currently in preparation by Maïthé Valles-Bled and Godelieve de Vlaminck sponsored by the Wildenstein Institute.

Notes: The present bouquet dates from *circa* 1909-10, at a time when de Vlaminck was influenced by Cézanne. Compared to his Fauvist still lifes, our picture marks a return to realism. The colours have assumed a more balanced and natural appearance. The vase, securely modelled with shade and a thick dab of white paint predictably functioning as a highlight, is placed on a table making use of traditional perspective. Yet, the heavy black outlines and the simplified *chiaroscuro* make the composition appear flat. He adopted Cézanne's principles of abstraction, but allowed himself great freedom in applying them. De Vlaminck's skills as a delicate colourist are beautifully demonstrated in our picture.

Before becoming an artist, he studied music himself. De Vlaminck was brought up at Le Vésinet near Paris. When he was called to enter military service, however, he was already sharing a studio with his close friend André Dérain. Up to 1907, he practiced the Fauvist style, but two major events, the Van Gogh exhibition of 1901 and the Cézanne retrospective of 1907, had, each in their turn, a decisive impact on his development. From the outset, he distanced himself from the prevailing Cubism and independently shaped his own personal energetic style of painting landscapes, still lifes and some portraits.

HERBERT FIEDLER (Leipzig 1891 - 1962 Amsterdam)
"A Clown in white holding his Saxophone"
Acrylic on triplex: 88,5 x 68,5 cm; signed and dated '58.

Provenance: collection P.H. Pruijt, The Hague; thence by descent.
Exhibition: Leiden, Stedelijk Museum de Lakenhal, "Herbert Fiedler", December 1965 - January 1966, cat. no. 31
(label on verso), on loan from P.H.Pruijt, The Hague.
Notes: Fiedler was born in Leipzig. Among his friends were George Grosz (1893-1959), Otto Dix (1891-1969), and Max Beckmann
(1884-1950). He studied at the academy in Dresden, 1909-1911, and at the Académie Julian in Paris between 1912 and 1914.
The influence of German expressionism is evident in his work. By the end of 1934, he felt threatened by the rise of fascism and moved to
Amsterdam, and later to Laren. When his house was confiscated in 1940, he moved to Amsterdam. Here, he often met with Max Beckmann.
Fiedler became a Dutch citizen in 1957. In 1958, he won the Sports Olympiad prize. His work can be found a.o. in the Stedelijk Museum
in Amsterdam, the Singer Museum of Laren, and the Museum Henriëtte Polak in Zutphen.

HENRI LEBASQUE (Champigné, Maine-et-Loire 1865 – 1937, Le Cannet, Alpes-Maritimes)
"The artist's daughter Marthe in a Hammock near the Mediteranean coast in Summertime"
Oil on canvas: 32,5 x 40,5 cm; signed (l.r.) and painted circa 1920.

Provenance: Hilde Gerst Gallery, New York, 1968; Mr George van Pelt, New York, purchased from the above; private collection, California.
Expertise: this painting is accompanied by a photo certificate from Denise Bazetoux, dated 21 -2-2005, and it will be included in her forthcoming catalogue raisonné on the artist; a certificate of authentication from Robert Martin accompanies the painting.
Notes: Lebasque went to Paris in 1886 to study with Léon Bonnat at the École des Beaux-Arts. In 1893, he had his first exhibition at the Salon des Artistes Indépendants, where he met Paul Signac and Maximilien Luce. He also became friends with Camille Pissarro, who gave Lebasque advice and encouragement. In 1903, Lebasque became one of the founding members of the Salon d'Automne, where he continued to exhibit for the rest of his life. He lived in Lagny-sur-Marne in 1905-1906, and painted along the banks of the Marne River in a style that combined elements of Impressionism and Pointillism. He later moved with his family to the South of France, eventually settling in Le Cannet on the Côte d'Azur. Given his love for the region, it is not surprising that he became enamored of the work of such artists as Henri Matisse, Raoul Dufy, Louis Valtat, and Pierre Bonnard, with whom he often shared a model. Henri Lebasque is known as a painter of the "good life", because his works customarily depict members of his family at leisure at home, on the terrace, in the garden, or by the seashore.
He was a sensitive colourist and this, in addition to his pleasing subject matter, accounts for his enduring appeal.

KONSTANTIN MATVEEVICH LOMYKIN (1924 - Odessa - 1994)
"At the Dance School, practising in front of the Mirror"
Oil on canvas: 110 x 100 cm; fully signed; on verso: signed, titled 'In front of the Mirror' and
inscribed 'All-Union Art exhibition', and dated 1970.

Provenance: directly from the artist's family estate.

Notes: This is one of the paintings that Lomykin made during or after his frequest visits to the Odessa Opera and Ballet Theatre. Ballerinas formed one of his most favourite subjects. In 1970, he sent it off to the important 'All-Union Art Exhibition' in that same year. Lomykin is considered a leading Odessa realist, and belongs to the top echelon of Russian painters. His wide ranging subject matter also includes colourful landscapes, portraits, any form of family life, and nudes. Furthermore, he was excellent in various painting techniques, such as pastels and watercolours. His realistic style of popular subjects, with impressionistic brushwork, and clarity in his subtle choice of colours, have gained him an international reputation. Already in the 1960's and 70's, Lomykin was asked to exhibit his works outside Russia, such as in Japan and the United States. The present painting is a good illustration of his virtuosity. In close association with Konstantin himself, his wife, as well as his daughter, have also been painting. It is therefore important to engage an expert when checking the authenticity of Lomykin's own work, and have its originality confirmed. Our Gallery has been dealing with Russian paintings of the Social-Realist and Impressionist Schools since the 1980's.

MICHAIL ARKADEVICH SUZDALTSEV (born in Suzdal 1917, active in Moscow)
"The First Wages"
Oil on canvas: 131 x 121 cm; signed and dated '57; on verso: signed and titled.

Provenance: from a Russian collection in Europe
Literature:' A Dictionary of twentieth century Russian and Soviet Painters 1900-1980's', Matthew Cullerne Bown, London, 1998;
Socialist Realist Painting, Matthew Cullerne Bown, London/New Haven 1998, with a reproduction of his painting 'To school Tomorrow'
(1951, Russian Ministry of Culture) on p. 251, plate 272.
Notes: Mikhail Suzdaltsev was born in Suzdal, near Vladimir, in 1917. He studied at the Odessa Art College from 1935 until 1938, and at the Surikov
Art Institute in Moscow in the period 1938 - 1948. Suzdaltsev lives and works in Moscow, and specializes in landscapes, and thematic and
genre paintings. He took part in several so-called brigade paintings, e.g. Dmitri Nalbandyan's (and brigade) 'Power to the Soviets,
Peace to the people' in 1950. He began exhibiting in 1948. Important shows include the *All Union Art Exhibition* in Moscow in 1949, 1950 and
1951, and *Soviet Russia*, in 1960, both in Moscow. In this important museum quality painting, Suzdaltsev was able to combine the all-Russian
realist theme. With great care, he allows us to witness a true family story, this time with an optimistic feeling, where the father gets home full of
pride, putting his first earned wages on the corner of the small table. His wife looks at him with deep and passionate feeling, realizing what must
pass through her husband's mind. The young boy, turning his head towards his dad in loving admiration, may well have just received the model
plane in his hands, as a gift to celebrate his dad's accomplishment.

ABRAM IOSIFOVICH VEKSLER (born in Kitaigorod, Ukraine, 1910 - 1982 Odessa)
"A busy Market Day in Odessa"
Oil on canvas: 188,5 x 151 cm; fully signed; on verso: signed, titled 'Odessa-Privoz'
(Odessa-Delivery), with the artist's address, and dated 1969.

Provenance: from a Russian immigrant collection in England.
Literature: 'A Dictionary of Twentieth Century Russian and Soviet Painters 1900-1980's', Matthew Cullerne Bown, London, 1998.
Notes: Veksler studied at the Odessa Art Institute between 1931 and 1936. He participated as early as 1936 in group exhibitions and one-man shows. At the same time, he was teaching art at the Kherson Art College. After the war, he became an art professor at his former Odessa Art College from 1946 until 1955. The present painting is a monumental document of the Realist style of painting from Odessa. Like his contemporary fellow painter Lomykin, Veksler too, loved using a clear technique with vivid impasto colours. His high vantage point allowed him to demonstrate the use of perspective that is so typically Russian, making sure that the hundreds of market vendors and shoppers somehow all fit onto the large canvas.

KONSTANTIN MEFODOVICH MAKSIMOV
(Ivanovo region 1913 - 1993 Moscow)
"Lacemakers from Pereslavl"
Mixed technique of gouache and pastel on board: 65 x 70 cm;
on verso: signed, titled 'Pereslavskie kruzhevnitsy. Eskiz', and
dated 1960.

*"A young Chinese Girl
with a Basket"*
Oil on canvas:
46 x 38 cm;
on verso: signed, titled
'Kitaika's korzinoi'
(Chinese Girl with
Basket), and dated 1956.

Provenance: from a Russian immigrant collection in Europe.
Literature: 'A Dictionary of twentieth century Russian and Soviet Painters 1900-1980's', by Matthew Cullerne Bown, London, 1998, with a.o. illustrations on page 195, plate 174 'A Graduation' (1960) and page 196 plate 175 'China, Boats in the port' (1958); Maksimov Moscow 1913-1993 / Beijng 1954-1957, an exhibition catalogue by the Cees Hogendoorn Gallery, Amsterdam 2001.

Notes: Maksimov is considered to be one of the most celebrated artists in the Soviet Union. He went to the Surikov Institute in Moscow (1937-1942), where he graduated from the studio of Georgi G.Riazhski. In 1950 and 1952, Maksimov won the Stalin prize for a series of portraits. One of his best-loved ones is '*Sasha, the Tractor driver*' of 1954, now in the Tretyakov Gallery in Moscow. In addition to portraits, he was also known for his genre-landscape- and still life paintings. In the late 1960's, he also experimented with watercolour. Maksimov took part in all the important *All-Union Art exhibitions* in Moscow since 1947, and in *Soviet Russia* in 1960. He had several personal exhibitions, his first at the age of 16 (!) in the hall of the People's House of Sereda. He worked as a professor at the Surikov Art Institute. His reputation was such, that in 1955 he was chosen to fulfill the important and artistic part of the extensive trade agreement between Russia and China, establishing the first Academy of the Arts in Bejing. He worked there as a teacher and advisor, and stayed for three years. His characteristic and lovely paintings from this period belong to the most sought-after in Russian art. The characteristic Chinese flavour in our present work, is a rare example of Maksimov's passionate capabilities. After his experiences in China, Maksimov travelled widely, including a few trips to Europe.

In the early 1960's, he visited the Pereslavl-Zaleski region extensively. These visits resulted in - among others - the painting of a large size canvas (160 x 295 cm) 'The Pereslavl Lacemaker', formerly in the museum collection of Kaliningrad. This present work is an advanced study for the same painting. Most of his oeuvre can now be seen in museums throughout the Soviet Republic.

Rembrandt

"Only those that go their own way, can never be overtaken"

CHRISTOFFEL BISSCHOP
(Leeuwarden 1828 - 1904 Scheveningen)
"Rembrandt arriving for the Anatomy Lesson of Dr. Tulp"
Oil on canvas: 86,5 x 131 cm; signed and painted circa 1864; with inscription in the door:
'Theatrum Anatomicum Collegium Chirurgium, 1619, Huc Tendimus omnes' (... where we are all headed).

Literature: W. Laanstra, "Johannes Christiaan Karel Klinkenberg 1852-1924, de meester van het zonnige stadsgezicht", Laren 2000, p.15 with ill.;
to be published soon in an article about Arti in 'Amstelodanum', a historical magazine about Amsterdam, by Drs. R. Daalder
Notes: In this painting, Rembrandt is about to start working on his renowned painting *The Anatomical Lesson of Dr. Nicolaes Tulp* (1632), and
demonstrates the affinity and fascination that Dutch society felt for national history, and the 'Golden Age' especially. This, in turn, led to the opening
in 1862 of a 'History Gallery', located at the premises of the Amsterdam artist association 'Arti et Amicitiae'. In 1864, Bisschop contributed the
present painting to this permanent exhibition. He portrayed himself in the painting as an assistant of Rembrandt's, whom he greatly admired.

"People that can laugh are never ugly"

A BRIEF OUTLINE OF REMBRANDT'S LIFE.

Rembrandt Harmensz. van Rijn (1606-1669) has become a part of global education, and has gained a prestige similar to products such as Coca Cola or Shell: almost every human being would know his name. In the Netherlands, we are proud of his reputation. Not so much for the constant beauty in all of his work, but rather for his never-ending stimulation through his oeuvre to keep us focused on discovering the many facets of our own character. Small though as we are as a country, in the person of Vincent van Gogh (1853-1890) we even have a number two in the world's top ten list. The content of both masters' artistic output does indeed tell a lot about the character of the Dutch. And to the ingredients of the down-to-earth Dutchman, we can add a colourful lining with the world's largest export trade of tulip bulbs.

In short, it seems that 'Art' is an expression of a society's culture at a given time in history. And it has been said that a 'genius' is formed in the whirling flow of this world. Only, it is much later in history that we realize the vision of these timeless talents. Therefore, I would like to add the fundamental difference between them and us, namely that a genius runs faster, ahead of his time, whereas we can hardly keep up with his development, even to the point when we are no longer able to understand him. It takes generations to realize that, long ago, a painter such as Rembrandt discovered the heart of the matter; that which is essentially human. In his case, it certainly is a profound bonding with the human soul and its sensitivities. Or, in other words: he was able to look deep into any person's soul, and illustrate in visual images what he experienced, without the inhibitions of time. In a way, his oeuvre became 'timeless'.

This to me seems the reason why other great masters such as Leonardo da Vinci, Michelangelo, Albrecht Dürer, Johannes Vermeer, William Turner, Picasso, and Jackson Pollock also demand our full attention. Such a group of exceptional master painters has always been and always will be, the focal point to any new development in society. Rembrandt's friend and intellectual Constantijn Huygens wrote in his diaries: "not even Apelles (one of the very first Greek painters) would have imagined what a young fellow, a Dutchman, the son of a miller, a beardless man, could muster and express". Huygens obviously had a visionary opinion then.

Rembrandt was born the ninth of ten children from the 'practical' marriage between a miller's son and a baker's daughter. Both had married in 1589 at the age of 21. When Rembrandt was born in Leiden in 1606, his parents were 38 years of age, rather old to present standards.

The Northern Dutch Provinces were engaged in the Eighty Years' War (1568-1648) with Spain. Prince William of Orange had been murdered in 1586, and the historical siege of Leiden had taken place in 1574. In addition, one of Holland's most important events would take place in 1602, when the V.O.C. (United East-Indian Company) was founded in Amsterdam, our first 'limited multi-national' company, later to be followed by giants such as Shell, Unilever, and Phillips. The trade of our Golden Age secured our roots, and supported the export from the Netherlands of the vast production of paintings. Rembrandt himself never travelled abroad, although he did passionately collect art and antiques from every culture. He spent liberally, and became known as 'the Grand Seigneur'. Still, you could say that he was the prototype of a purely Dutch product.

Rembrandt attended Prep school, and then called the Latin school, which would enable him to go to Leiden University, but he never did. He preferred pursuing the arts, with a preference for painting and, between the ages of 13 to 16, did an apprenticeship with two important painters (Jacob van Swanenburgh and Pieter Lastman). Already at the age of 17, he started out on his own in Leiden. He remained there until 1631, and then moved to Amsterdam. Here, one could earn more income with the painting of historical subjects. However, to support his lifestyle, Rembrandt would still have to supplement his income with the production of portraits for the nobility. He entered into a business relationship with the art dealer Hendrick Uylenburgh, and in 1632 he received his first important painting commission, *The Anatomy Lesson of Professor Tulp'*. In 1634 he married Uylenburgh's cousin Saskia, who came from Friesland.

Together, they had two sons and two daughters. Only Titus, born in 1641, survived. Meanwhile, Rembrandt created the *'Night Watch'*, a painting completed in 1642. In that same year, his wife Saskia died and a nanny, Geertje Dircks, entered his household to help him bring up the infant Titus. Although Geertje claimed that Rembrandt had promised to marry her, they never did and in 1649 she was hospitalised in a psychiatric clinic. At the same time he completes *'The Hundred Guilder Print'*.
Another nanny, Hendrickje Stoffels, took her place. She did not marry Rembrandt either, but yet in 1654, they did have an illegitimate daughter Cornelia.
In the same year and with a substantial mortgage, Rembrandt became the owner of the present 'Rembrandt house' in the St.Antoniebreestraat, but three years later was forced to sell the house and all of its belongings. He moved his family to the Rozengracht in the Jordaan, still a folkloristic part of today's Amsterdam. Around 1660 Hendrickje and Titus acquired the rights to all of Rembrandt's work.

Critics of his time called Rembrandt 'a miser'. This was well illustrated by an anecdote of a practical joke on the part of his students. They painted gold coins on the floor of his studio, which the money-devouring master regularly tried to pick up from the floor!
Hendrickje died in 1663, and his son Titus married in February 1668, only to die six months later, barely 27 years old. His wife was pregnant at the time, and in March 1669 Rembrandt became the godfather to his first and only grandchild, Titia. Unfortunately, he did not enjoy his grandparental role for long, because half a year later Rembrandt himself died and was buried in the Westerkerk, near his house. One month after his death, still in 1669, his daughter-in-law also passed away.
With such a sad family history, it is no miracle that Rembrandt had to deal with much grief and sadness. However, he was able to bend his life's struggle into a positive and artistic stimulation of his oeuvre, thus nurturing his gifted talent. In my opinion, this constant search for creativity must have been his personal therapy.

In the bourgeois society of 17th century Holland, the Church and the aristocracy slowly disappeared as the sole commissioners of the arts. And Rembrandt had difficulty in identifying himself with the new upper classes of society. This group was particularly keen on still-lifes and landscapes to adorn their homes with. He himself had been mainly trained as a history painter, and felt this to be his main artistic asset. Period portraits were only executed out of necessity, for money. But even when he landed a contract for a historical painting, the demands of these commissions rarely matched Rembrandt's ambitions.

Hardly any other painter in history has painted so many self-portraits, in which he painstakingly studied every facial expression over and over again. The self-portraits gave a mirror image of Rembrandt's own spirit and soul.

After his death, Rembrandt drifted into obscurity. The fashion of the day favoured a polished sensual form of art and artistry, in clear and bright colours. The art of Rembrandt was seen as being too coarse, too unfinished, and not sufficiently sublime. It was only during the Rococo period in the second half of the 18th century, when the arts were experienced as being bittersweet, that the need for a less contrived and a more earthly approach caused a revival of Rembrandt's work.

And it was not until 1852, that a monument for Rembrandt was finally erected. It can still be seen in the Rembrandt Square in Amsterdam. At the time, there were suggestions that this monument was being erected for the honour and glory of the nation itself rather than for Rembrandt. In any case, from the 19th century onwards, **Rembrandt has been frequently called 'the Shakespeare of Painting".**

At the start of the 20th century, over 1000 paintings had been authenticated as being genuine Rembrandts. And in 1906, one of the art historians joked: "please do not discover any more Rembrandts, but bring Rembrandt to us, Oh Lord". By 1935, his oeuvre had been gradually reduced to 630 works. And in the 1960's, experts selectively put the total at between 400 and 500 paintings.

Finally, in 1969, the Rembrandt Research Project (RRP) was launched. This group, made up of international art historians and a technical staff, is still actively searching for clues in order to stylistically and technically evaluate all of the Rembrandts and their attributions. In all, they may not even go beyond 300 'authentic' Rembrandt paintings.

Sensational to the general public as part of this grand-scale investigation was undoubtedly the rejection of the famous so-called 'Polish Rider' in the Frick Museum in New York, and the 'Man with the Golden Helmet' in the Berlin Museum. From the start, the RRP was also being seen as controversial. Apart from the loss of valuable capital and prestige, the criticism being directed at this team of experts may have some validity. According to other art historians, their starting points are stylistically too narrow, too qualitative and most of all too scientific.

The differences of opinion and the approach underline the complexity of reaching the essence of what can be considered the 'real' Rembrandt, eventually most probably reduced to ten percent of the cases. And to give you an idea of this complex research project, the handwriting experts of the Forensic Laboratory in the Netherlands some years ago were convinced that sixty percent of the 'genuine' Rembrandt paintings carried a 'false' signature.

Rembrandt had many students (perhaps as many as forty or fifty), who were also participating in the production of a 'real' Rembrandt. Novices were not accepted. Competent pupils needed to have been educated in this profession, and pay a tuition fee to the tune of 'one hundred guilders' per annum.

To ensure everybody's focus, Rembrandt fitted the attic of his studio with partitions. You could hear, but not see one another. On one occasion, this working space concept yielded one of the few examples of his coarse humour. Behind a partition, Rembrandt overheard a student say to his model "…now we are just like Adam and Eve in Paradise, both in the nude…". And Rembrandt shouted: "… and just because you are naked, I will throw you out of Paradise…!", after which he disciplined the naughty rascal and perhaps ordered him to start drawing ginger jars!

A student did not enter his Studio to simply develop his own personality, but to learn and dream Rembrandt's own method. **"Conscientiously apply what you have learned, and during this process, you might discover the secrets and nuances of this fine profession"** is what Rembrandt used to preach.

REMBRANDT HARMENSZ. VAN RIJN
(Leiden 1606-1669 Amsterdam)

"Self Portrait with Saskia"
signed and dated: *Rembrandt. f. 1636*

etching: 104 x 95 mm; trimmed on or just outside the platemark

Bartsch 19; Seidlitz 19; Hind 144; **White-Boon 19, first state (of three)**
Plate in existence – with Nowell-Usticke (1967): C2-
Condition: an excellent and well balanced 17th century impression

Provenance: from a private Dutch collection.

The original and modernistic concept of this self portrait together with Saskia, is of an extraordinary, innovative character. Over the centuries, it has proved itself to be of a timeless quality, and no doubt, it still serves as a great example to modern photography.

In this etching, the thirty year old Rembrandt portrayed himself confidently looking up, while drawing, or possibly in the process of making an etching. Because of the mirror image of the impression from the original plate, he seems to have become a left-hander. Rembrandt wears a 16th century barret with a brim showing slits.
Rembrandt has often painted and drawn his wife Saskia, whom he married just two years earlier. However, of his entire graphic oeuvre, this is the only portrait of Rembrandt together with his wife Saskia van Uylenburgh.

Since this was a popular print, many publishers have copied this image over the centuries. At least six different types of copies are known, and even a few from which the image of Saskia has been removed. The first state of this etching can be easily recognised by the curved slipped stroke above Saskia's right eyebrow.

"A Self-Portrait with Plumed Cap in an Oval"
signed and dated: *Rembrandt f. 1634*

etching: 130 x 105 mm; with at least 3 mm margins;
watermark: Arms of Württemberg (Ash & Fletcher p. 66, B'.a.)

Bartsch 23; Seidlitz 23; Hind 110; **White-Boon 23, third state (of three)**
Plate not in existence – with Nowell-Usticke (1967): C1+
Condition: a strong and velvet 17th century impression

Provenance: Julian Marshall, London (Lugt 1494); James Reiss, Manchester and London (Lugt 1522);
Paul Davidsohn, Berlin (Lugt 654), his sale 1920, no.15; Maurice Gobin; private collection, Paris.

This is a very fine, early impression of the third state (of the original plate with square-cut corners).
Both the fancy appearance of the model and the fact that only a small edition of this etching seems to have been printed make the identification as a self-portrait most likely, even if Rembrandt remains nearly unrecognizable in his disguise as an oriental soldier (Filedt Kok). The plate started out as a full-length portrait, with the sitter holding a lowered sabre. In the third state, possibly as a result of damage to the plate, it was made into a regular oval. The three states must have been quite close in date for, according to Ash and Fletcher, the Arms of Württemberg watermarks, one of which appears on this impression of the third state, are found on seven different etchings, all signed and dated in the early 1630s.

"Abraham and Isaac"
signed and dated: *Rembrant. 1645.*

etching and burin: 157 x 130 mm; platemark still visible at the top and partly on the left, trimmed just along the bottom and right-hand side; watermark: at present difficult to identify

Bartsch 34; Seidlitz 34; Hind 214; **White-Boon 34, only state**
Plate in existence – with Nowell-Usticke (1967): C2+
Condition: a beautifully even and delicate late 17th century impression

Provenance: on verso: various numbers in pencil; Jan Hendrik Jurriaanse, 1866-Rotterdam-1940, (Lugt 1403b supplément); from a private Dutch collection.

White and Boon describe only one state of this etching, but the differences between the states as described by Biörklund-Barnard are quite clear. In the first state, the top platemark is not square and the arched line is continuous. In the second, the platemark is filed down to a square, thus cutting into the line of the arch. Research has shown that there are more significant changes between first and second state hitherto unrecorded.
In the light of this newfound evidence, we can conclude that the present image is a very good and delicate impression of the 'new' second state. Some burr is still visible, and lends a warm and luminous effect to the quality of this impression.

REMBRANDT HARMENSZ. VAN RIJN
(Leiden 1606-1669 Amsterdam)

"The Angel appearing to the Shepherds"
signed and dated: *Rembrandt. f. 1634*

etching, burin and drypoint: 262 x 218 mm; with good margins; watermark: Foolscap

Bartsch 44; Seidlitz 44; Hind 120; **White-Boon 44, third state (of three)**
Plate in existence - with Nowell-Usticke (1967): C2-
Condition: a beautifully inked and balanced 17th century impression

Provenance: from a private Rhenish collection.

When Rembrandt created *The Angel Appearing to the Shepherds,* it was undoubtedly his most spectacular print to date. Both its composition and technique separate it from his other prints of the early 1630s. His desire to create a rich nocturnal landscape may have been stimulated by the engravings of Hendrick Goudt after Adam Elsheimer, while the dramatic events can perhaps be better compared to contemporary Baroque painting rather than printmaking.
Christopher White (*Rembrandt as an Etcher: A Study of the artist at work, London 1969, pp.38 - 39)* describes it as a watershed in Rembrandt's career, and goes on to say: 'As an original work in the medium it is the artist's most successful expression of the baroque style. The technique is elaborate, but it just escapes being overstrained. He achieved the richness of tone for which he sought, and gave the plate a quality which is essentially that of etching and not a mere approximation of a painting. In doing so he had abandoned traditional methods, and the procedure he evolved in this print was to colour his work for some years hence, culminating in that great turning point in his career, *The Hundred Guilder Print'*.

A superb impression on this subject, certainly among the finest: the celestial light from the sky strikes the amazed shepherds and their startled beasts. It also illuminated the tips of the branches of the trees, which seem to shine out from the encircling night. In contrast to this dazzle, the distant landscape seems to glint under the rays of a gentle moonlight.
By any standards, this etching is a tour-de-force, and especially so for an artist at the early stages of his career. In that same year 1634, Rembrandt must have felt exuberant, because of his marriage to his first wife Saskia van Uylenburgh.
Of the first state, some five impressions of the unfinished plate are known, all in museum collections. The present example must be one of the earliest pulls for the completer (third) state, comparing very well, in terms of richness and lack of wear, with the fine second states in London and Vienna. The landscape, subject to the earliest wear, is still intact and free of abrasions.

In the night, there appeared to the herdsmen in the field an angel, who brought them the tidings of the birth of Christ. 'And suddenly there was with the angel a multitude of the heavenly host praising God, and saying, Glory to God in the highest, and on earth peace, good will toward men' (Luke 2:8-14). The herdsmen and their animals, scattering in terror at this apparition, are tiny figures in the grandly conceived landscape. Rembrandt has fully exploited the dramatic contrast between the light in the sky and in the foreground, and the surrounding gloom of the night.

"The Adoration of the Shepherds: with the Lamp"
signed *Rembrandt. f* circa 1654

etching and burin: 105 x 129 mm; platemark still visible

Bartsch 45; Seidlitz 45; Hind 273; **White-Boon 45, second state (of two)**
Plate in existence – with Nowell-Usticke (1967): C2-
Condition: a 17ᵗʰ century impression rich in tonality

A beautifully strong print with burr throughout the extensively worked shadow parts, cut along the still visible plate mark. Old mounting traces, but otherwise the print is fresh and well preserved. In this second state, the white strip at the border was worked over with the burin. This impression in this condition is very rare.

After the announcement of the birth of the Messiah, the shepherds went to Bethlehem, where they found Joseph and the Virgin, and the newborn child in the crib (Luke 2:15-16). The simple, spontaneous manner of etching is well suited to the intimate nature of the scene.

This print seems to be the nicest representation of the birth of Christ. Already in Rembrandt's lifetime, it sold well. It probably belongs to a series about the youth of Christ: these sheets (White-Boon 45, 47, 55, 60, 63, 64, and 65) are of almost identical dimensions, and together they make a thematic and stylistic combination.

"The Circumcision in the Stable"

signed and dated twice (in the signature in the upper left, the 'd' is reversed) *Rembrandt f 1654*

etching: 94 x 144 mm; with good margins

Bartsch 47; Seidlitz 47; Hind 274; **White-Boon 47, first state (of two)**
Plate in existence – with Nowell-Usticke (1967): C2-
Condition: an excellent and rich 17th century impression

This print is part of a group of etchings, all of the same size (Wh.-B. 45, 55, 60, 63 and 64), showing scenes from the childhood of Christ. All images belonging to this group are tender and unpretentious, and at the same time excellent in the facility of the technique. Such beautiful hand proofs of this artist, using plate tone for light and dark effects, are extremely rare. This magnificent first state impression is rich with burr, and with at least a margin of 4 mm around the edges of the plate. In contrast to the second state, blank spaces appear immediately below the signature in the top left-hand corner, and along the top border immediately above the Child.

When the infant Christ was a week old, *the time came to circumcise him, and he was given the name of Jesus* (Luke 2: 21). The circumcision was required by Mosaic Law as a token of the Covenant, and might be performed by the parents or by a priest in the Temple especially designated for this purpose. A mother is not allowed to enter a Temple until she has been purified, 40 days after the birth of her child. However, the circumcision must take place on the eighth day, so a site other than a synagogue would be preferable. The iconographic tradition normally sets the scene in the Temple. Rembrandt chose to depict this scene in a stable, creating a very intimate atmosphere.

REMBRANDT HARMENSZ. VAN RIJN
(Leiden 1606 – 1669 Amsterdam)

"Christ disputing with the Doctors"
signed and dated: *Rembrandt. f. 1652*

etching and drypoint: 126 x 214 mm; with good margins

Bartsch 65; Seidlitz 65; Hind 257; **White-Boon 65, second state (of three)**
Plate not in existence - with Nowell-Usticke (1967): C2+
Condition: an excellent and rich 17th century impression

Provenance: from the Prince Soutzo collection (Lugt 2341).

This Bible scene, in which the young Jesus, aged twelve, debates with the teachers of the scriptures in the temple (Luke 2:46-7), precedes the return to Nazareth (White-Boon 60). Both prints are part of the series on the youth of Christ, referred to in the commentary of *The Adoration of the Shepherds : with the Lamp*.
The subject *Christ disputing with the Doctors* was close to Rembrandt's heart: he used it as a subject for several etchings as well as a number of drawings. It gave him an oppurtunity to use his considerable powers of invention in portraying the scholars' sceptical reactions to the arguments of the self-assured boy.

"Christ driving the Money-Changers out of the Temple"
signed and dated: *Rembrandt. f. 1635'*

etching: 136 x 169 mm; with narrow margins around the borderline; watermark: Foolscap

Bartsch 69; Seidlitz 69; Hind 126; **White-Boon 69, second state (of two)**
Plate in existence – with Nowell-Usticke (1967): C2-
Condition: an excellent 17ᵗʰ century impression

Beautiful, outstanding, and clear print of the first state, before the additional work on the mouth and soles of the man in the right foreground, dragged by a cow.
With narrow margins around the borderline. With insignificant separate corrections in both left corners, and only some scattered foxing. In all other respects, the print is in very good condition.

When Jesus entered the temple during the feast of the Passover, he found moneychangers, and men buying and selling oxen and sheep. He made a whip of rope and drove all of them and their beasts out of the temple, overturning the moneychangers' tables (John 2:13-17).

"The Raising of Lazarus" the small plate;
signed and dated: *'Rembrandt f 1642'*

etching, with some drypoint: 150 x 114 mm; trimmed on the platemark;
watermark: Arms of Amsterdam

Bartsch 72; Seidlitz 72; Hind 198; **White-Boon 72, first state (of two)**
Plate in existence – with Nowell-Usticke (1967): C2-
Condition: a very strong and rich 17th century impression

Provenance: Mr. G. Rapilly, Paris, purchased in 1921 by the Duke of Buccleuch (Lugt 402).

The present work is completely different from the baroque piece done in 1632, and was created in the year of Saskia's death. The gestures and expressions of shock are far more restrained, and the lighting is far less dramatic. A very strong, rich and early impression with patches of drypoint and burr, which must have disappeared soon after the first series of impressions had been printed. When Jesus heard that Lazarus, the brother of Mary and Martha, had died, he traveled to Bethany, where he resurrected the dead man. By that time, Lazarus had already been buried for four days (John 11:1-44).

REMBRANDT HARMENSZ. VAN RIJN
(Leiden 1606 – 1669 Amsterdam)

" The Hundred Guilder Print"
finished circa 1649

etching, burin, and drypoint: 278 x 388 mm; with extremely wide margins;
watermark: Lily of Strasbourg (Ash & Fletcher B.b)

Bartsch 74; Seidlitz 74; Hind 236; **White-Boon 74, second state (of two)**
Plate cut up in approx. 1776 by Captain Baillie – with Nowell-Usticke (1967): C1-
Condition: a formidable and beautifully toned 17th century impression

Provenance: Francis C.Gray, inventory no.3238, (Lugt 1101);
Fogg Art Museum duplicate , Harvard University (Lugt 936); from a private Dutch collection.

Rather than depicting a single episode of Christ's preaching, Rembrandt has chosen to illustrate virtually all of Matthew XIX. Thus, one sees from left to right the Pharisees, with whom Christ debated the questions of marriage and divorce; the rich young man, whom Christ advised to sell his possessions to benefit the poor; the little children, whom he asked to be brought to him; the paralytic woman, whom he healed, and perhaps others as well. The etching style ranges from the sketchiness of the Pharisees to the finished and rich chiaroscuro of the figures to the right, which has caused commentators to date Rembrandt's earliest work on the print anywhere from 1639 to 1647 (though all agree that it was completed in 1649). There are a number of sketches of these different groups, showing various thoughts Rembrandt had before he was finally satisfied. In the centre is Christ, who visually and logically holds the composition together. Rembrandt's revisions of this figure are evident in the fine web of lines that chart the face and body, giving Jesus a truly otherwordly glow.

A magnificent and extraordinary, well-balanced impression, reading especially well in the dark areas. This is partly due to the high quality and the tone of the paper and also to the fact that the burr, especially in the left half of the plate, is still intact throughout. The margins are exceptionally wide, adding force to a marvellous richness of this important print.
Visually, the only difference between this second and the first state is the extra drypoint on the various figures and the crouching dog in the left foreground, which was obviously burnished down by Rembrandt, because their strong accents were too distracting to the eye.

Christopher White (in *Rembrandt as an Etcher,* p.55) refers to the *Hundred Guilder Print* as the 'apotheosis of Rembrandt's activity in etching in the 1640's, and according to popular opinion of his whole career'. The etching was highly regarded from the seventeenth century onward, as its informal title bears witness to. There are several conflicting anecdotes as to how the name *Hundred Guilder Print* came about, the most popular one being Gersaint's, in the eighteenth century, which was probably based on an inscription on the verso of an impression in the Rijksmuseum. According to that note, Rembrandt exchanged a copy of the etching for several prints by Marcantonio Raimondi, valued at 100 guilders by a Roman art dealer. *The Hundred Guilder Print*, common in middle or late pulls, is exceedingly rare in truly early impressions. It goes without saying that it is only by looking at the best examples that one can appreciate the technical brilliance and the spiritual content of this famous print. Various impressions of the first and second state have been printed on different types of paper, such as white European and Japan paper.
The plate was acquired by Captain William Baillie in 1735, and reworked. After publishing a number of impressions from the original large plate, he cut it up in 1776 into four individual parts. Of these four parts, Baillie also printed impressions.

REMBRANDT HARMENSZ. VAN RIJN
(Leiden 1606 – 1669 Amsterdam)

"Christ crucified between the two thieves:
The Three Crosses"
signed and dated: *Rembrandt. f .1653*

etching, drypoint and burin: 385 x 450 mm; with good margins

Bartsch 78; Seidlitz 78; Hind 270; **White-Boon 78, fourth state (of five)**
Plate not in existence – with Nowell-Usticke (1967): R+
Condition: a superb and richly toned 17th century impression of this large plate

Provenance: C. & R. Hirschler (Lugt 633a), purchased from Gilhofer and Ranschberg, 1926; from a private collection.

In the earlier states of this plate, the centre of the image is bathed in light radiating from the top of the plate. In the fourth state, Rembrandt transformed the print by introducing heavy shading lines in this area and also at the sides. He also burnished out much of the earlier work, and removed or redrew many of the figures. The two thieves are now shrouded in gloom, and the one on the left is partly hidden behind a horseman with a tall hat, inspired by a Pisanello medal. The focus is now almost entirely on the lonely figure of the suffering Christ in the upper centre of the image. The effect of chiaroscuro gives this image a more dramatic appearance than in the earlier states.
The radical changes between the three earlier states and this fourth one may well be proof of Rembrandt's compassion for the history of the Bible. It is suggested that this particular plate has been reworked and dramatised by him, some seven years later.

This is a fine, openly printed impression of this state, with good drypoint burr. It reads well, especially in the darker areas (which sometimes get clogged with ink), and the surface still has a freshly printed appearance. The large size of the plate underlines the monumentality of this impressive historical subject matter.

Early in his career, with the help of another etcher, Jan Joris van Vliet, Rembrandt produced three very large, upright plates of *The Descent from the Cross* (two versions both dated 1633, one spoilt in the biting) and *Christ Shown to the People* (1635), possibly emulating the engravings after Rubens's designs. In 1639, he followed these with a large, but entirely autographed etching of *The Death of the Virgin*. However, throughout his career, Rembrandt normally worked on a medium or small scale. The two very large, oblong drypoints, *The Three Crosses* and *Christ Shown to the People* of 1653 and 1655, are the only really large-scale works of his later career. To produce these drypoint masterpieces on such a scale required consummate skill in the use of the medium.

REMBRANDT HARMENSZ. VAN RIJN
(Leiden 1606-1669 Amsterdam)

"The Baptism of the Eunuch"
signed and dated: *Rembrandt. f 1641*

etching and some burin 178 x 213 mm; with narrow margins

Bartsch 98; Seidlitz 98; Hind 182; **White-Boon 98, second state (of two);**
(Note that White-Boon's only illustration - of a second state impression -
appears to be incorrectly labeled as a first state.)
Plate in existence – with Nowell-Usticke (1967): C2-
Condition: an exceptional 17th century impression with beautiful contrast

Philip the Evangelist had been charged by an angel to take the road from Jerusalem to Gaza. Once there, he met a Eunuch, a dignitary of the Ethiopian court. Philip converted him and baptized him in a body of water they happened to be passing (Acts 8:26-39).

This is a very fine impression with subtle contrasts, of the second (final) state, with the additional lines added to the waterfall and bank at right with the burin, with delicate polishing scratches showing in the sky and background, with narrow margins all around (except at top right, where it has been trimmed to the platemark).

Rembrandt must have been impressed by a composition of his teacher's Pieter Lastman (circa 1583-1633), and already as early as 1626 he used the same subject matter in a beautiful and colourful painting, now in Museum Catharijneconvent in Utrecht. Could it be a coincidence that this fine print was created in the same year as the birth of Rembrandt's son Titus?

REMBRANDT HARMENSZ. VAN RIJN
(Leiden 1606-1669 Amsterdam)

"The Death of the Virgin"
signed and dated *'Rembrandt f.1639'*

etching and drypoint: 409 x 315 mm; with good margins

Bartsch 99; Seidlitz 99 third state (of five); Hind 161;
White-Boon 99, second state of three
Plate possibly lost after Basan – with Nowell-Usticke (1967): C2-
Condition: a very detailed and excellent 17th century impression

Provenance: with collector's information in almost illegible handwriting on the verso.

This etching in the second state goes back to before the addition of vertical shading of the foremost bedpost in the third state. The white tablet in the lower corner, probably intended for an inscription, was frequently cut off, but in this case it has been preserved completely, with fine paper margins all around it. Such a well-conserved print as this one is very rare. In this second state, the chair was heavily shaded with drypoint.
According to Seidlitz, together with the *One-Hundred-Guilder print*, this etching is the most magnificent of all of Rembrandt's oeuvre of etchings. It is an outstanding example of the use of chiaroscuro, one of his favourite techniques.

The account of the death of the Virgin does not appear in the New Testament, only in the apocryphal literature. Rembrandt has borrowed a number of elements from Dürer's woodcuts of the birth and death of the Virgin.

REMBRANDT HARMENSZ. VAN RIJN
(Leiden 1606-1669 Amsterdam)

"St. Jerome Reading in a Landscape"
signed (lower left) and dated (lower right) *Rembrandt f.1634*

etching: 108 x 90 mm; complete with thread margins all around

Bartsch 100; Seidlitz 100; Hind 119; **White-Boon 100, only state**
Plate not in existence – with Nowell-Usticke (1967): R+
Condition: a very clear and beautiful 17th century impression

Provenance: Ambroise Firmin-Didot (1790-1876) (Lugt 119); Hulot (A. Hulot? – see Lugt no. 2040), according to a note on the former mount, it was purchased on the 7th of February 1921 from Monsieur G. Rapilly, print dealer at the Quay Malaquais in Paris for 600 francs.

This is a rare and delicate etching, with burr, in a fairly early impression. Only Ludwig Münz, in 1952, suggested the participation of Joris van Vliet in this print. However, the vituosity of the dry-point technique in this intricate subject-matter has always been recognized as entirely characteristic of Rembrandt.
Rembrandt shows the moment of the legend when the lion looks in horror at the carcass of the donkey, after he was wrongly accused by St. Jerome of having killed and eaten his friend. The donkey had in fact been stolen and later the lion was forgiven.

REMBRANDT HARMENSZ. VAN RIJN
(Leiden 1606-1669 Amsterdam)

"The Ship of Fortune"
signed and dated: *Rembrandt. f. 1633.*

etching: 111 x 166 mm; with wide margins;
watermark: Crowned double C with Cross of Lorraine

Bartsch 111; Seidlitz 111; Hind 106; **White-Boon 111, second state (of two)**
Plate not in existence – with Nowell Usticke (1967): R
Condition: an excellent and very early 17th century impression

Provenance: Paul Davidsohn (Lugt 654), his sale, Leipzig (C.G. Boerner), 26th-29th April 1921, lot no. 103 (described as *Ausgezeichneter Abdruck*); C. Gaa (no mark), his sale, Leipzig (C.G. Boerner)' 1926, lot no. 777; Arie Johannes Lamme (Lugt 138), Joseph Ritman, Amsterdam, his sale at Sotheby's 1995, lot no. 61.

This etching was used as an illustration to E. Herckmans' *Der Zee-Vaert Lof* ('The Praise of Seafaring'), published in Amsterdam in 1634. It appears in chapter 3, which deals with Mark Antony's defeat in the battle of Actium in 31 B.C.. Fortune, the nude woman on the ship, is turning her back on Mark Antony, sitting on his fallen horse and gesturing in desperation. In the background, the temple of Janus, traditionally depicted as a bust with two faces looking in opposite directions, is being closed as a result of these events and as a symbol of peace. In the left foreground, seated on the fallen charger, we see the emperor Augustus wearing a laurel wreath. The female figure hoisting the sail is probably Bellona, the goddess of war and sister of Mars, god of war, perhaps the man sitting at the stern. With peace having been declared, they can now leave the battlefield. Some authors regard the female figure as the goddess Fortune.

The other seventeen etchings in the volume were made by Willem Basse. Elsewhere in his book, Herckmans explains that the coming of peace will lead to a new flourishing of the sea trade.
The only Rembrandt print in this book was inserted as the twelfth illustration, right at the beginning of the third volume.

This is an excellent impression, a very early proof and printed prior to its inclusion in the book. It is set off by generous margins, and is printed with good tone. The only one known impression of the first state, before the plate was cut at the left, is in the Bibliothèque Nationale, Paris.

DER
ZEE-VAERT LOF,
Derde Boeck.

Ellone [a] (die te gaer met Mars te velde torsten
't Gehamerd yser, tot bescherm, van buyck en borsten:
Wen sabels blixems-flagh, tot dond'rend' veld-geschrey
Iav'lijn en flitsen stroyd op Mavors oorloghs rey)
Verbied (om weynigh rusts en adem locht te scheppen)
'T allarm trompets geluyt en 't nare brand-klocks kleppen
Te water en te land, beyd' krijger en matroos;
So langh, tot nieuwe twist heur ftael ten [b] rechter koos.
Weshalven dat de vorst [c] Auguft' de heyl'ge tempel
Des achterfienden [d] Gods doet fluyten, aen den drempel

ANNO MVNDI
3935.
Ætat. Rome 723.
a Bellone, de fufter van Mars, beyde God ende Goddinne des oorloghs.
b Wanneer tuffchen twee partyen twiften op-ftaen, ende fich onder malkander door beenden niet vergelijcke konnen, kiefen ghemeenlijck den degen van Mars en Bello-

ne, om hun fcheydtman te wefen, diens degen dan langft is, diens rechte alder-grootft is, fo de wijfe Seneca feydt: Ius eft in armis, opprimit leges pudor. c Ottavius Cæfar Auguftus, Monarcha ende Roomfch Keyfer, d Den achterfienden God van Ianus, die eertijds by den Heydenen eenen koninck ghewccft is, den eerften Politicus, ofte Burgerlijcken, die het grote woorfte ende rouwe leven der menfchen verfultende tot een eerdijcke fachte en zeckelijcke burgherlijckheyd van leven, daeromme hem eerft de Romeynen als eenen half God ghe-eerd, ende naruabs Numa Pompilius hem eenen tempel ter eeren gheboudt heeft, hem met twee aenfichten uytbeeldende, te weten, met het achterfte fiende op de voorgaende rowe manier van leven, en met het voorfte aengericht fien-de op 't gene dat afterde door hem verfiem, ofte verbetert was, door welcke manier van leven de hyden verdelijck malkanderen beminden, daerom hem de Romeynen in tijd des oorlogha ghedurtigh offenden, want als de

N   De

REMBRANDT HARMENSZ. VAN RIJN
(Leiden 1606-1669 Amsterdam)

"The large Lion Hunt"
signed and dated *Rembrandt f 1641*

etching with drypoint and burin: 224 x 300 mm; with good margins;
watermark: Strasbourg Lily and Countermark WK (Ash & Fletcher 36.E'.a)

Bartsch 114; Seidlitz 114; Hind 181; **White-Boon 114, second state (of two)**
Plate not in existence – with Nowell-Usticke (1967): RRR-
Condition: a beautiful and toned 17th century impression

Provenance: British Museum Duplicate (Lugt 300 and 305).

This is an extremely rare and outstanding impression of the second (final) state, with the head of the horse to the extreme right now closely shaded with the burin, and printed with a delicate plate tone, with nice margins. Of the first state, there are only three recorded examples, now in museum collections, but the change in state is not very significant.

Rembrandt made three etchings of lion hunts: *The Small Lion Hunt with Two Lions* and *The Small Lion Hunt with One Lion,* all very much influenced by the work of Rubens and etching by Antonio Tempesta. In this, the latest and the largest, Rembrandt has gone far beyond his model, in both composition and technique. He has drawn the figures with bold open lines, partly cutting off those on the left and right to add to the sense of urgency and motion.

"Three Oriental Figures (Jacob and Laban?)"
signed and dated (in reverse) *Rembrandt f 1641*

etching and drypoint: 145 x 114 mm; with narrow margins

Bartsch 118; Seidlitz 118; Hind 183; **White-Boon 118, second state (of two)**
Plate in existence – with Nowell-Usticke (1967): C2-
Condition: an unusually strong 17th century impression

Provenance: from a southern German private collection.

This is an excellent and clear impression with deep, contrasting features overall. The delicate craquelure in the sky and the fine plate tone, are genuine characteristics of an early impression. With narrow margins all around. At this stage, foliage was added to the right of the porch.

The scene depicted here may be the argument between Jacob and Laban: Jacob wishing to return to Canaan with his wives Leah and Rachel and his children, but his father-in-law Laban trying to dissuade him (Gen.30:25-34).

In his oeuvre catalogue of 1922, Seidlitz added the suggestion that this print, catalogued in the inventory of the Rembrandt publisher Clement de Jonghe, could be the one with the title *Pratertjes aan de deur* (Gossiping at the door).

"The Rat Catcher"

signed in monogram and dated: *RHL 1632* (the last two numbers in reverse)

etching: 140 x 125 mm; with thread margins
watermark: with initials of Nicolas Heussler

Bartsch 121 ; Seidlitz 121; Hind 97; **White-Boon 121, third state (of three)**
Plate not in existence – with Nowell-Usticke (1967): R
Condition: an exquisitely detailed and clear 17th century impression

Provenance: Atherton Curtis (Lugt 94); from a private Dutch collection.

On the top of a pole, the rat catcher carries a basket containing live rats. As proof of the efficiency of the poison being peddled, dead animals are hanging from under the basket. The rat catcher himself looks rather impressive in his thick coat, wearing a tall cap, with big strong hands, a bearded and expressive face, and armed with a sabre hanging from his belt. To add to his imposing figure, a sizeable rat sits happily on his left shoulder. The delicate lighting in this etching enhances the overall velvet tonality. The young boy, standing between the rat catcher and his costumer, is holding a large box possibly containing the poison. The subtle use of light on his face gives an attractive charm to this scene. The elderly customer seems to talk back to someone in the house, deliberating whether they should make use of the rat catcher. This print was extremely popular in the 17th century. The plate, however, did not survive, and beautiful impressions such as this one are extremely rare.

"The Goldsmith"
signed and dated: *Rembrandt f. 1655*

etching and drypoint: 77 x 56 mm; complete with narrow margins

Bartsch 123; Seidlitz 123; Hind 285; **White-Boon 123, first state (of two)**
Plate in existence – with Nowell-Usticke (1967): C2
Condition: an excellent and clear 17th century impression

Provenance: on verso: with a double stamp of Tomas Harris; from a private Dutch collection.

After a number of etchings with biblical scenes from the period between 1633 and 1655, this seems to be the first and only print with a subject from daily life. Here, we see the Goldsmith putting the final touches to a figure of Caritas, the personification of Charity.
In the left foreground, some of his specialised tools, and in the background the forge.
A year later, in 1656, Rembrandt etched the portrait of the Goldsmith Jan Lutma from Amsterdam.

This etching has been printed on different kinds of paper, such as laid and Japan paper.
It can be seen as an excellent example of how Rembrandt experimented to achieve different effects of tonality and finesse.

"Woman at a Door Hatch talking to a Man and Children (The Schoolmaster)"
signed and dated: *Rembrandt f 1641*

etching 93 x 61 mm; with narrow margins;
watermark: City of Amsterdam

Bartsch 128; Seidlitz 128; Hind 192; **White-Boon 128, only state**
Plate in existence – with Nowell-Usticke (1967): C2+
Condition: an exquisite, even, and clear 17th century impression

Provenance: Collector's stamp (not in Lugt); from a southern German private collection.

An excellent impression from the early and only state before the changes added to the later additions in drypoint, with Watelet. In Amsterdam there is an impression on Japan paper.
Even though Nowell-Usticke classifies this print as fairly common, it is nonetheless 'rare' to find this print in such a fine condition, on 17th century laid paper.

"The Quacksalver"
signed and dated: *Rembrandt. f.1635*

etching 78 x 36 mm; trimmed just within the platemark

Bartsch 129; Seidlitz 129; Hind 139; **White-Boon 129, only state**
Plate not in existence – with Nowell-Usticke (1967): RR-
Condition: a delicate and clear 17th century impression

Provenance: Jean-Baptiste-Eugène Gallice, Epernay, (Lugt 1063 with the date "1870", see also Lugt 855); private collection, Paris.

Quite a few of Rembrandt's early etchings represent beggars and street characters. The quacksalver selling elixirs and specifics (remedies intended for a particular ailment or disorder) often drew the satirical barbs of 17th century printmakers, draftsmen and painters. They are generally loaded down with crocks and bottles, but there can be no doubt that Rembrandt's lightly laden figure is also a quacksalver. As usual, the figure is dressed ludicrously in dandified clothes that are decades out of date. In our opinion, the quacksalver holds a pair of spectacles in his left hand. Could it be that both Rembrandt and the quacksalver consciously, and in an amusing way, intended to symbolise well-known proverbs such as: 'looking through someone else's glasses' and 'looking at the world from a different perspective'.

A very good impression of what Nowell-Usticke calls "a very scarce, desirable little print." This etching rarely prints this strong, the present impression is beautifully clear. It is rare to find this delicate quality, even showing horizontal polishing scratches. It is trimmed just within the platemark, and slightly into the image at the left.

"A peasant Family on the tramp"
circa 1652

etching: 113 x 93 mm; complete with 2-3 mm margins

Bartsch 131; Seidlitz 131; Hind 259; **White-Boon 131, first state (of two)**

Plate in existence – with Nowell-Usticke (1967): C2
Condition: a soft and delicately toned 17th century impression

Provenance: William S. Pelletier collection, Georgia, with collector's stamp;
from a private Dutch collection.

This impression is of excellent quality. In this first state, there is a small area of false biting on the man's pack and along his belt. This image looks very much like a drawing. Here, Rembrandt used much detail in the figure of the peasant, and a more fleeting approach in the child and the mother. This seemingly easy technique seems typical of his ability to create an attractive image. At the lower right, there are remnants of an old man's head.

Rembrandt Harmensz. van Rijn
(Leiden 1606-1669 Amsterdam)

"Beggars Receiving Alms at the Door of a House"
signed and dated: *Rembrandt. f. 1648*

etching, burin and drypoint: 165 x 128 mm; with complete 2 mm margins

Bartsch 176; Seidlitz 176; Hind 233; **White-Boon 176, first state (of three)**
Plate in existence – with Nowell-Usticke (1967): C1-
Condition: an exquisite and superb 17th century impression

Provenance: Baron D. Vivant-Denon (1747-1828) (Lugt 738);
A. Freiherr von Lanna (1836-1909) (Lugt 2773).

This is an exquisite and brilliant impression in a superb condition, with nice burr. In contrast to the second state, and clearly visible, is the absence of the four short vertical lines shading the white spot on the back of the almsgiver's cap.

The quality of this print on white paper enhances the clarity of this touching subject matter. There is a fascinating contrast between the deeper blacks and the lighter tonalities, which together support the overwhelming sense of brightness.

This etching is perhaps one of Rembrandt's most moving depictions of ordinary life, and it is certainly one of his most celebrated prints. The grouping of the beggar's family around the door, the distinctiveness of the man giving alms, emphasised by the closed half-door, the gully underneath it, and the absence of any background, all contribute to remind the spectator of the humane nature of the act of alms-giving. Undoubtedly, Rembrandt's sensitivity has not overlooked the intimate, almost private human exchange, adding a mystical quality to this scene. The supreme mastery is that Rembrandt can make the spectator feel that he is actually there, standing directly behind the little boy, an observer unobserved.

It is no wonder that such a beautiful impression of this moving image has always been highly desired by important collectors. The provenance already indicates previous owners such as Vivant-Denon, the director of the Musées Impériaux in Paris, and Freiherr von Lanna from Prague. The latter's impressive collection was sold after his death in no less than five separate auctions.

REMBRANDT HARMENSZ. VAN RIJN
(Leiden 1606 – 1669 Amsterdam)

"A Peasant calling out: *Tis vinnich kout"*
titled, signed and dated: *Rembrandt f 1634*

and

"A Peasant replying: *Dats niet"*
titled, signed and dated: *Rembran(dt) f 163(4)*

etching 112 x 43 and 112 x 39 mm; both trimmed just on or within the platemark

Bartsch 177 & 178; Seidlitz 177 & 178; Hind 114 & 115;
White-Boon 177 & 178, both only states
Plate not in existence – with Nowell-Usticke (1967): both RR-
Condition: both are strong and superb 17th century impressions

Provenance: Pierre-Jean Mariette, Paris, 1694-1774, (Lugt 1852);
Anthony C. (de) Poggi, London, died around 1836 (Lugt 617);
unidentified collection (Lugt 900); from a private Dutch collection.

This is an expressive illustration showing two peasants discussing the weather. Rembrandt has put much character into both of them, who seem to stand along the edge of frozen water. It is amusing that they conduct their conversation standing back to back. Clearly, the left figure appears to feel the cold, whereas the man on the right does not seem to be affected by the sometimes vicious Dutch winters.
In this same year, Rembrandt married Saskia, the cousin of his art dealer Hendrick Uylenburgh.

It is extremely rare to find such beautiful and clear impressions of both etchings together. They are extremely desirable to any Rembrandt print collector.

REMBRANDT HARMENSZ. VAN RIJN
(Leiden 1606 – 1669 Amsterdam)

"Diana at the Bath"
signed *RHL.f.* and circa 1631

etching: 178 x 159 mm; with good margins;
watermark: Double-headed eagle (Ash & Fletcher 15 Aa)

Bartsch 201; Seidlitz 201; Hind 42; **White-Boon 201, only state**
Plate not in existence – with Nowell-Usticke (1967): R+
Condition: an excellent 17th century impression with rich contrast

Provenance: William Esdaile (1758-1837), London, in 1811 (Lugt 2617);
with an unidentified collector's mark, in pencil, recto and verso;
from a private Dutch collection.

In 1631, at about the time of Rembrandt's move from Leiden to Amsterdam, he made a small group of prints and drawings of the female nude. Much to the dismay of some 17th and 18th century critics, these meticulous studies from life eschewed all classicising conventions and portrayed the sitters in an unidealised, naturalistic state. Although Rembrandt has added a classical context to the etching, including a bow and quiver to identify the figure as Diana, this is clearly a study of a model in the studio. At this early stage in his printmaking career, Rembrandt is still feeling his way with the etching needle, but here he has admirably caught the surprise on the face of Diana, disturbed while bathing in a stream.

The present impression is well balanced and delicately printed, with a subtle sense of clarity. On laid paper, with a faint crease at the bottom right and some minor discoloration along the margins.

This is one of the rare cases in which a prepatory drawing for the etching exists. It is a study in chalk and brown wash, preserved in the British Museum (Benesch 21). All the main elements of the composition are there, and Rembrandt has traced the outline with a stylus in order to transfer the design onto the ground of the etching plate.

REMBRANDT HARMENSZ. VAN RIJN
(Leiden 1606 – 1669 Amsterdam)

"View of Amsterdam from the North West"
circa 1640

etching, with traces of sulphur: 112 x 153 mm; trimmed just along the platemark

Bartsch 210; Seidlitz 210; Hind 176; **White-Boon 210, only state**
Plate not in existence – with Nowell-Usticke (1967): R-
Condition: a very delicate 17th century impression with burr

Provenance: from the John Barnard Collection (Lugt 1419).

Here, Rembrandt has etched the city from the North-West. The view is taken from the Kadijk and, in a mirror image of the actual scene, shows from left to right: the Haringpakkerstoren, the Oude Kerk, the Montelbaanstoren, the East and West India Co. warehouses, the Mill on the Rijzenhoofd and the Zuiderkerk. The view shows neither the West India Co. warehouse, built in 1642, nor the Waleneiland, laid out in 1644. The silhouette of the city is carefully drawn, though it has of course been reversed by the printing process. Because of the low viewpoint, the darkly detailed foreground becomes more prominent in the scene and the skyline of the city stands in sharp contrast to the horizon.

The exquisite print, executed around 1640, can be seen as the master's first landscape etching. In those days, Rembrandt's popularity was huge, and to date this rare and panoramic view of Amsterdam is very much sought after.

A very good impression with light vertical polishing scratches in the sky, especially to the right. Trimmed along the platemark on three sides, and just within the platemark at the bottom.

This impression was formerly owned by the 18th century London collector John Barnard (died 1784), whom Lugt calls "un des meilleurs juges de son époque en matière d'art". On the verso of this very fine impression, he marked his initials and Rembrandt's name "à la plume".

REMBRANDT HARMENSZ. VAN RIJN
(Leiden 1606 – 1669 Amsterdam)

"The three Trees"
signed and dated: *Rembrandt f 1643*
(partly hidden in the lower left corner, but in this impression clearly visible)

etching, with drypoint and burin: 213 x 279 mm; complete with good margins;
watermark: a Crowned Lily with initials WK,
consistent with those only found in fine early impressions
(cf. cat. "Rembrandt, Experimental Etcher", Boston 1969, p 181, ill.1)

Bartsch 212; Seidlitz 212; Hind 205; **White-Boon 212, only state**
Plate not in existence – with Nowell-Usticke (1967): RR-
Condition: a most wonderful 17th impression with fascinating contrast and burr

Provenance: from a private Dutch collection.

This etching is Rembrandt's most celebrated landscape, the only one executed in 1643.
The threatening sky is most unusual for Rembrandt's etched landscapes. The thunderclouds and the false sunlight produce a dramatic contrast. The naturalistic features of the moment could lead us to suspect/expect the appearance of a rainbow at any moment. From the dike with its three tall trees, a flat expanse stretches away into the distance, populated by numerous tiny figures. The silhouette on the horizon is probably taken from the vicinity of Amsterdam, near the Haarlemmerdijk, to the west of the city. In the left foreground a peasant couple is fishing, and to the right, suggestively hidden behind some bushes, a young courting couple. The drama and solidity of these three formidable trees, in combination with Rembrandt's dedication to the Bible, might be suggestive of the idea that Rembrandt flirted with the illusion of Mount Calvary with the three crosses.

In the clouds to the left, remnants of an earlier study can be recognized, but they may not be from Rembrandt's hand. It is very well possible that the plate belonged to another etcher, before it might have passed on to Rembrandt, while the original surface had not yet been polished off properly.

This extremely rare impression of superb quality, with its rich tonalities in the darker areas adding a sense of velvet coloration, makes us aware of the immense reality of nature.
The middle fold is flattened, some light stains, small tears along the margins restored, and a faint brown ink outline to indicate the platemark.

REMBRANDT HARMENSZ. VAN RIJN
(Leiden 1606 – 1669 Amsterdam)

"Landscape with a square Tower"
signed and dated: *Rembrandt f 1650*

etching and drypoint: 88 x 156 mm; trimmed just outside the platemark,
and along the arched plate corners at the top

Bartsch 218; Seidlitz 218; Hind 245; **White-Boon 218, fourth state (of four)**
Plate not in existence – with Nowell-Usticke (1967): RR-
Condition: a very delicately toned 17th century impression

Provenance: from a Canadian collection.

This early and rare impression in the fourth and final state, clearly shows the slipped stroke through the signature and the polishing scratches in the sky. These very fine diagonal lines create a sense of drizzle in the background of this delicate landscape. This deceptively simple composition depends for the most part on the effect of the distribution of drypoint. The existing burr accentuates the shadows cast by the strong sunlight.

In this impression, it almost seems as if Rembrandt experimented with the warm colour of the paper, to create a natural atmosphere with contrast: not just of light and shade, but also of dry and wet. Some thin spots are scattered in the sky.

Rembrandt Harmensz. van Rijn
(Leiden 1606 – 1669 Amsterdam)

"Landscape with a Cottage and a Haybarn"
signed and dated: *Rembrandt f. 1641*

etching: 129 x 321 mm; complete with narrow margins

Bartsch 225; Seidlitz 225; Hind 177; **White-Boon 225, only state**
Plate not in existence – with Nowell-Usticke (1967): R-
Condition: a superb and wonderfully balanced 17th century impression

Provenance: from a private Dutch collection.

In 1641, Rembrandt executed two landscape etchings of similar oblong size (White-Boon 225 and 226), both depicting the outskirts of Amsterdam. The view on the left is probably based on Amsterdam, the house and the trees on the right have been identified as 'Kostverloren', on the river Amstel. In about 1650, 'Kostverloren' burnt down and not until much later was it rebuilt, and renamed 'Ruyschenstein'.

This is one of Rembrandt's most famous and highly-prized landscapes. The composition is very well balanced, with Rembrandt revelling in the use of elaborate perspective, giving this view a panoramic sense of space. The farm and haybarn in the foreground are exceptionally detailed. He always loved to wander along the river Amstel, and he must have socialised with many of the locals. The two young boys fishing, the man strolling over a little bridge followed by his dog, and the woman looking out of the window, give it a true sense of intimacy and family life.

REMBRANDT HARMENSZ. VAN RIJN
(Leiden 1606-1669 Amsterdam)

"Landscape with a Cottage and a large Tree"
signed and dated: *Rembrandt. f. 1641*

etching 127 x 320 mm; with complete 2 mm margins;
watermark: Strasbourg Lily (Ash and Fletcher v36 B.d -1641),
consistent with those only found in the earliest impressions

Bartsch 226; Seidlitz 226; Hind 178; **White-Boon 226, only state;**
"new" first state, as described by C.P. Schneider, 'Rembrandt's Landscapes: Drawings and Prints',
National Gallery of Art, Washington, 1990, no. 5, before the shadows in the tall tree on the left are
darkened in the 1650s with a technique similar to sulphur tinting.
Plate not in existence – with Nowell-Usticke (1967): R-
Condition: a superb and exciting 17th century impression

Provenance: on the verso: with black chalk numbers and a date of 1762 in an 18th century hand;
private collector, 20th century, Boston; to the estate of the same.

Apart from the discovery of Cynthia Schneider, the polishing scratches and the delicate plate tone emphasize the significance of this rare and early impression. There is no sign of wear, and the clarity of line accentuates the beautiful quality of this impression.

In 1641, Rembrandt made two landscape etchings of the vicinity of Amsterdam. Both images are almost equal in size and belong to his largest landscape prints. Here, he has chosen to depict a sizeable farm set in the foreground of a typically flat Dutch landscape. The cottage and tree, the two children playing at the door, the two ducks along the water side, and other elements that appear close to the viewer are very deeply bitten, while the distant town has been only lightly etched. Rembrandt would have covered this latter area and then re-immersed the plate into acid in order to create this sharp contrast between foreground and background. It is a technique he gradually abandoned in his later prints, preferring other ways of creating this sense of distance.

REMBRANDT HARMENSZ. VAN RIJN
(Leiden 1606 – 1669 Amsterdam)

"Faust in his Study"
circa 1652

etching, drypoint and burin: 210 x 160 mm; with excellent margins

Bartsch 270; Seidlitz 270; Hind 260; **White-Boon 270, first state (of three)**
Plate in existence – with Nowell-Usticke (1967): C2+
Condition: a superb 17th century impression on brilliant white European paper

Provenance: Princes of Liechtenstein (until 1959); Donald A Karshan;
Kimbell Art Foundation, Fort Worth, Texas, sale in New York (Sotheby's),
15th May 1987, lot no.56;Joseph Ritman, Amsterdam,
his sale at Sotheby's, 1995, lot no.103.

The subject of this etching remains something of a mystery, despite the best efforts of scholars and collectors. The present title, *Faust in his Study*, first appeared in the inventory of the Delft collector Valerius Röver in 1731, and has been widely used ever since. However, there are no passages in Marlowe's *Doctor Faustus*, which appeared in 1588, that correspond to the scene depicted here. In the 17th century, the print was known as *The Practising Alchemist*, or at least that was the title in the inventory of Clement de Jonghe's collection. The print, however, does not conform to the traditional representation of alchemists, and the shining disk, with its inscription INRI and the surrounding anagram, has yet to be satisfactorily explained, although its source has been identified.

Whatever its exact meaning, Rembrandt's etching is a masterful depiction of an elderly scholar in his study. Obviously interrupted from his work, for he still holds his pen in his right hand, he is transfixed by the apparition that has appeared before him. This spectral light is quite different from the light that filters in through the window at the rear, and the scholar's rapt immobility is balanced by the agitation of the mysterious drapery above his head.

A very fine impression on brilliant white European paper, in total contrast with the impression on oatmeal, (Ritman catalogue no. 104). Here the highlights, notably the shining disk, are accentuated by the pure white paper. And the mid-tones and the darker drypoint shadows are all beautifully articulated.

REMBRANDT HARMENSZ. VAN RIJN
(Leiden 1606 – 1669 Amsterdam)

"Clement de Jonghe, Printseller"
signed and dated *Rembrandt f. 1651*

etching and drypoint: 207 x 161 mm; with fine margins

Bartsch 272; Seidlitz 272; Hind 251; **White-Boon 272, first state (of six)**
Plate in existence – with Nowell-Usticke (1967): C2-
Condition: a unique and early 17th century impression

Provenance: Jan Chalon (Lugt 439), his daughter married Christian Josi, the well-known print dealer; from them, the Chalon collection of Rembrandts was purchased, via Thomas Philipe, by Reginald Pole Carew, and dispersed at the Carew sale, London (Mr. Wheatley), 13th - 15th May 1835, lot 279; presumably bought by Edward Vernon Utterson (Lugt 909), his sale, London (Christie's), 17th February 1848, lot 81 (described as second state); Sale, New York (Sotheby's), 11th November 1981, lot 860; Joseph Ritman, Amsterdam, his sale at Sotheby's 1995 lot no. 75.

Clement de Jonghe was one of the most respected publishers and print dealers, located in the Kalverstraat in Amsterdam. He was active between 1640 until his death in about 1677. A few years later in 1679, an inventory was made of his estate, and among the possessions were over 70 copper plates that Rembrandt had etched. Among others, he published prints by Roelant Roghman and Jan Lievens.

In this image, the sitter is portrayed as a man of distinction, and has a coyful expression.

This impression is without question the finest we have ever seen, superior even to the British Museum's impression of the first state on Japan paper. It is darkly printed with strong background tone and a large thumbprint in the upper left corner, in fact showing all the qualities of an exceedingly early proof. This print has a special presence, a combination of strength and delicacy which makes a very great impact.

And according to Nowell-Usticke 'the early states are very desirable and much sought after.'

REMBRANDT HARMENSZ. VAN RIJN
(Leiden 1606 – 1669 Amsterdam)

"Jan Lutma, Goldsmith"
signed and dated (in the second state): *Rembrandt f.1656*

etching, drypoint and burin: 196 x 150 mm; with excellent 18 mm margins;
watermark: traces of the Lily of Strasbourg

Bartsch 276; Seidlitz 276; Hind 290; **White-Boon 276, second state (of three)**
Plate in existence – with Nowell-Usticke (1967): C2-
Condition: an exquisite and luminous 17th century impression

In the second state of this print, Rembrandt profoundly changed the setting, adding a deep niche with a window behind the figure of Lutma. This increased the apparent space and markedly darkened the whole setting. The changes in the third state are minimal and may not be by Rembrandt.

This luminous impression is, as far as we can ascertain, the very best example of the finished state of this portrait. Rembrandt's personal touch is conspicuously evident here, among others, in his careful inking of the plate, which diminishes the contrast between high light and deep shadow, and focuses attention on the old man sitting in his chair. This pictorial wiping is particularly notable in the window panes, where a veil of tone gives a slight opacity to the clear glass. White-Boon records five examples printed on Japan paper. This seems to be the richest and earliest of the group.
In its subtle modulation of tone, this impression is quite different from the stark immediacy of the first (unfinished) state.

Born in Groningen in 1584, Jan Lutma died in the same year as Rembrandt, in 1669. He was one of the most renowned goldsmiths in Amsterdam. Rembrandt depicts him in 1656 at the age of 72, sitting in a leather armchair holding a small statue in his right hand. Some goldsmith's tools are on the table on the right-hand side. In the second state, Rembrandt signed and dated the plate in the upper left-hand pane of the window. On the right-hand side, an inscription (probably not by Rembrandt) tells us the name of the person portrayed. Jan Lutma's son, also an etcher, may have been responsible for the inscription of his father's name in the second state, just above the engravers' tools on the table.
Most likely this portrait was commissioned by the sitter.

REMBRANDT HARMENSZ. VAN RIJN
(Leiden 1606 – 1669 Amsterdam)

"Jan Uytenbogaert, Preacher of the Remonstrants"
signed and dated in the third state: *Rembrandt . ft 1635*

etching and burin: octagon shape 224 x 187 mm; with thread margins;
watermark: Lily of Strasbourg and WR (Heywood 141).

Bartsch 279; Seidlitz 279; Hind 128; **White-Boon 279, fifth state (of six)**
Plate in existence – with Nowell-Usticke (1967): C1+
Condition: an excellent and clear 17th century impression

Provenance: from a private Dutch collection.

together with the original copperplate!

Octagonal, etched copperplate: 224 x 187 mm, with irregular plate edge along the bottom;
etching and burin technique (in the second state), with the addition of the signature,
date and four verses by Grotius (in the third state).

Exhibition: North Carolina Museum of Art, Raleigh, USA, in 1956 (Humber collection);
Rembrandthuis, Amsterdam, May-June 1993.

Provenance: after Rembrandt's death in 1669, possibly directly purchased by Clement de Jonghe,
Rembrandt's friend and publisher, where the plates were first mentioned in his posthumous
inventory in 1679; for the exact history of this copperplate, we refer to our chapter
'A brief history of Rembrandt's copperplates' (p. 156).

The preacher Jan Uytenbogaert (1557-1644) was one of the leaders of the Remonstrants, also called the Arminians. They were the followers of Jacobus Arminius, who believed in the more liberal religious doctrine set out in the Remonstrance of 1610. However, the Synod of Dordrecht (1618/19) removed all Arminians from their posts and sent many into exile. Uytenbogaert went to Antwerp and was able to return to The Hague in 1626, thanks partly to the intervention of Prince Frederick Henry (whose teacher he once was).

In 1635, this was Rembrandt's first official commission for an etched portrait. It is also one of his few portrait etchings to have a caption: a rather carelessly etched panegyric in Latin by Hugo Grotius, the Arminians' most important political leader and a friend of Uytenbogaert's. He was the first person in 17th century Holland to stress the importance of international law.

REMBRANDT HARMENSZ. VAN RIJN
(Leiden 1606 – 1669 Amsterdam)

"Lieven Willemsz. van Coppenol, Writing-Master" the smaller plate; circa 1658

etching, drypoint and burin: 258 x 190 mm; with narrow margins

Bartsch 282; Seidlitz 282; Hind 269; **White-Boon 282, third state (of six)**
Plate not in existence – with Nowell-Usticke (1967): RRR-
Condition: an exquisite and subtly toned 17th century impression

Provenance: The Rev. A. E. Goddard; Sir Francis Seymour Haden (Lugt 1227);
his sale, Sotheby's London, 15th June 1891, lot 430;
(described as from the Barnard collection, presumably mixed up
with A. E. Goddard's pen and ink signature on the verso).

This rare and early impression of the amusing portrait of the writing-master and his grandson, is delicately executed and with good burr. In the fourth state, the circular disc above the boy's head, is replaced by a triptych with a crucifixion, hanging on the wall.

Lieven Willemsz. van Coppenol (1599- after 1667) was head of the French School in Amsterdam. In 1650, he suffered an attack of insanity, after which he was no longer allowed to teach. He then turned to working as a professional calligrapher, and travelled around Holland giving demonstrations. Rembrandt depicts Coppenol here just after he has completed a freehand circle, regarded as a proof of his competence with the pen. The boy in the background is Coppenol's grandson Antonius.

"Bald-headed Man in Profile right: small bust; possibly the Artist's Father (?)"
signed and dated *RHL 1630*

etching: 57 x 43 mm; with wide margins

Bartsch 294; Seidlitz 294; Hind 24; **White-Boon 294, only state**
Plate not in existence – with Nowell-Usticke (1967): RRR-
Condition: a rare and beautiful 17ᵗʰ century impression

Provenance: Hermann Weber, 1817 till 1854 in Bonn, (Lugt 1383); his sale,
Leipzig (R. Weigel), April 1856, lot 422; Kunsthalle, Mannheim, sold 1938;
auction in Bern (Gutekunst & Klipstein), 6th October 1950, lot 440;
Dr. Friedrich A. Lieberg (not in Lugt), sale in Bern (Kornfeld & Klipstein), 21st June 1979,
lot 109; Joseph Ritman, Amsterdam, his sale at Sotheby's 1995, lot nr. 113.

During his years in Leiden, Rembrandt made a number of portraits in etching and in painting, using studio models as well as members of his family. This print has been thought to represent the artist's father, Herman Gerritz van Rijn, who died in 1630. While there is no concrete evidence to support the identification, it belongs to a group of small portrait studies which are amongst the most penetrating and subtle of those etched by Rembrandt in those years.

This lightly etched plate can only have yielded a handful of really good impressions, but the present example has all the fine, delicate lines modelling the face that are characteristic of them.

"A Man Wearing a Close Cap: Bust Portrait, possibly the Artist's Father"
1630

etching and burin: 75 x 60 mm; with splendid margins

Bartsch 304; Seidlitz 304; Hind 21; **White-Boon 304, fourth state (of five)**
Plate not in existence – with Nowell-Usticke (1967): RR
Condition: an extremely strong and clear 17th century impression

Provenance: Carl J. Kollmann, 1820 till 1875 in Dresden (Lugt 1585); sold in his estate auction, Dresden (Rud.Meyer), February 1877;Dr. August Sträter (Lugt 787), his sale, Stuttgart (Gutekunst), 10th-14th May 1898, lot 859; Franz von Hagens (Lugt 1052a), sale, Leipzig (C.G. Boerner), 27th-28th May 1927, lot 482; Frits Lugt (Lugt 1028); Dr. Friedrich A. Lieberg, 1947 (not in Lugt), his sale in Bern (Kornfeld & Klipstein), 21st June 1979, lot 111; Joseph Ritman, Amsterdam, his sale at Sotheby's, 1995, lot 114.

The original plate size was 97 x 73 mm, with the signature and date along the bottom margin. In the third state, the plate was cut down to the present size, and a monogram and date were added at the top left. The background remained blank. In this fourth state, the background was added, and the monogram and date almost became invisible underneath the cross-hatching. This is a very rare and strongly inked impression on paper with very wide margins. The features of the sitter, thought to be Rembrandt's father Harmen Gerritsz. van Rijn, convey great character.
Scholars differ as to whether one of Rembrandt's pupils may have retouched this print in a later state, possibly the fifth. Could it be that White-Boon and others mistakenly used the word 'close' instead of 'cloth' in the title?

"The Artist's Mother in a Cloth Headdress, looking down: Head Only"
signed and dated *Rembrandt. f. 1633*

etching: 42 x 40 mm; with good margins

Bartsch 351; Seidlitz 351; Hind 107; **White-Boon 351, second state (of two)**
Plate not in existence - with Nowell-Usticke (1967): RR+
Condition: a delicate and very fine 17th century impression

Provenance: According to a note on the back of the former frame,
the impression was bought for 100 francs from Collignon, rue de Seine, Paris,
in 1919 and was once in the collection of E. M. Signol

Rembrandt had left Leiden in 1631, and he probably made this little plate on a return visit, possibly to introduce to his family his fiancée Saskia van Uylenburgh. As in the case of the etching of his mother in a cloth headdress of 1628 (she died in September 1640), Rembrandt etched the face first, and most of the headdress was only added in the second state of the plate. Again, he had difficulty in balancing the biting of the two states, but this time the final result was more successful.

This is a very good impression with perfect margins, which are somewhat dust-marked along the platemark.

**"Sheet of studies: Head of the Artist, a Beggar Couple,
Heads of an Old Man and Old Woman, etc."**
circa 1632

etching: 100 x 105 mm; complete with 2 mm margins

Bartsch 363; Seidlitz 363; Hind 90; **White-Boon 363, second state (of two)**
Plate not in existence –with Nowell-Usticke (1967): RR+
Condition: an excellent and clear 17th century impression

Most of the sheets of sketches were done by Rembrandt between 1632 and 1638.
He used the etching plate as a leaf out of a sketchbook. They often contain various motifs, such as portraits (mostly of Saskia) and studies of beggars and peasants. Each of these study plates have been used from different angles.

The characteristic self-portrait shows Rembrandt at about the age of 26.
The beggar couple, very delicately portrayed, seem more like an elderly couple leaning on sticks. In addition, there are two sketches of an older man with a cap, and a woman with her headdress.
Sheets of studies like these would not have been included in the usual assortment of Rembrandt prints on offer.

In this second state, the foul biting was removed and the plate reduced in size. With plate tone, this is a very fine impression of this rare print.

"Three Heads of Women: one Asleep"
signed and dated: *Rembrandt f 1637*

etching: 143 x 97 mm; complete with thread margins all around
watermark: Arms of Bristol (Ash & Fletcher 4.A and 4.A.a)

Bartsch 368; Seidlitz 368; Hind 152; **White-Boon 368, only state**
Plate in existence – with Nowell-Usticke (1967): C1
Condition: an excellent and clear 17th century impression

Provenance: from a private collection, Paris.

The woman depicted twice on the right is probably Saskia, Rembrandt's wife. The young Saskia, at the age of twenty-five, is beautifully portrayed by her husband. The fact that Saskia's health has been weak throughout her life, did not keep Rembrandt from lending youthful determination to her facial expressions. She died in 1642 at the age of thirty, never having recovered her health after the birth of Titus, her only child to survive beyond the age of two months. This is an excellent impression, still showing some polishing scratches and plate tone. The darker shadows, still showing some burr, enhance the clarity of this image.

"Sheet of Studies, with a Woman lying ill in Bed, etc."
circa 1641/42

etching: 136 x 151 mm (!); with thread margins and sometimes trimmed on the platemark

Bartsch 369; Seidlitz 369; Hind 163; **White-Boon 369, only state**
Plate not in existence - with Nowell-Usticke (1967): RR+
Condition: a beautiful and lucid 17th century impression

Provenance: "D" drystamp: possibly either Drake (Lugt 723) or Daulby (Lugt 736a);
Moritz von Kuffner, Vienna (not in Lugt); thence by descent.

Probably because of the intimate subject matter, it is one of the rarer sketch-plates. This study-plate has two very moving portraits of Saskia lying in bed, and clearly not well. During her marriage, Saskia had four confinements, and she died of tuberculosis in 1642, at the age of thirty. Her son Titus, born in 1641, was the only child to live to adulthood. The so-called studies of two different elderly couples and a distinguished woman, do not just seem to be simple sketches. In fact, the serene gestures of all five figures and their precise character, positioned around both of Saskia's images, suggest the drama of the cross Rembrandt had to bear. It almost seems as if Rembrandt portrayed his own parents and his parents in law, visiting Saskia while she was ill and after she had passed away. This subject can easily be seen as a unique family tribute. This very delicate impression with the effective burr and light plate tone from the rare print, creates a sense of extreme beauty and devoted intimacy.

"Self-portrait in a Cap and Scarf with the Face dark"
signed and dated: *Rembrandt f. 1633*

etching: 132 x 103 mm;
trimmed just within the platemark

Bartsch 17; Seidlitz 17; Hind 108;
White-Boon 17, second state (of two)
Plate in existence –
with Nowell-Usticke (1967): C2-
Condition: a fine and clear late 17th century impression

Provenance: from a private Dutch collection.

Due to the popularity of this youthful self-portrait, executed in the year of his engagement to Saskia van Uylenburgh, the plate has been frequently retouched by the many publishers since Rembrandt. It is unique, in any case, to find a self-portrait, with his face almost completely in dark shadows.

"Abraham entertaining the Angels"
signed and dated: *Rembrandt f. 1656*

etching and drypoint:159 x 131 mm;
with good margins;

Bartsch 29; Seidlitz 29; Hind 286;
White-Boon 29, only state
Plate lost after Rembrandt's death –
with Nowell-Usticke (1967): C1-
Condition: an superb 17th century impression with delicate tones and burr

Provenance: from a private Dutch collection.

The three angels are being entertained by Abraham, to whom they promise that his wife Sarah, already well on in years, will soon bear a son.
The composition is broadly similar to that of a drawing done by Rembrandt at about the same time (Benesch 1187), in which he copied a Mogul miniatiure 1627/ 28 showing four sheiks in conversation.

"Virgin and Child in the Clouds"

signed and dated: *Rembrandt f. 1641*

etching and drypoint: 168 x 106 mm;
complete with 2 mm margins;
watermark: Lily of Strasbourg with 'PR"
(in Ash & Fletcher)

Bartsch 61; Seidlitz 61; Hind 186;
White-Boon 61, only state
Plate not in existence –
with Nowell-Usticke (1967): C1+
Condition: an exquisite and tonal 17th century impression

Provenance: Charles Delanglade, Marseille (Lugt 660);
from a private Dutch collection.

This Catholic theme, rare in 17th century Dutch art, must have originated from an Italian influence such as Federico Barocci's. The subject of 'mother and child' is hardly surprising to come across in the same year that Rembrandt's only son Titus was born.

"The good Samaritan"

signed and dated (in the 4th state):
Rembrandt. inventor et Feecit. (sic.) 1633.

etching and burin: 257 x 208 mm;
trimmed just outside and on the platemark

Bartsch 90; Seidlitz 90; Hind101;
White-Boon 90, fourth state (of four)
Plate lost after Rembrandt's death –
with Nowell-Usticke (1967): R+
Condition: an excellent and well-balanced
17th century impression

Provenance: on recto: Alexander Hunter,
early 19th century, United Kingdom (Lugt
2306); from a private Dutch collection.

On the same subject, a grisaille from 1632 is exhibited in the Wallace collection, London, and there seems to be a drawing in Hamburg, both in reverse. This image could have been inspired by a Simon de Vlieger painting.

"The Star of the Kings: a night piece" circa 1651

etching, and drypoint: 94 x 143 mm; trimmed just within the platemark; a counter proof impression

Bartsch 113; Seidlitz 113; Hind 254;
White-Boon 113, only state; very rare:
White-Boon refers to only three counterproofs
Plate in existence – Nowell-Usticke (1967): C2+,
Condition: a slightly vague, yet detailed late 17th century impression

A counter proof was customary for the artist and his publisher. It served as a working specimen to visualise the necessary corrections to the plate in the correct direction of the image.

"A peasant in a high Cap, standing and leaning on a Stick"
signed and dated: *Rembrandt f. 1639*

etching: 83 x 45 mm; complete with 2 mm margins

Bartsch 133; Seidlitz 133; Hind 164; **White-Boon 133, only state**
Plate in existence – with Nowell-Usticke (1967): C1
Condition: a fine, delicate, and detailed 17th century impression

Provenance: from a private Dutch collection.

In 1639, Rembrandt purchased the present Rembrandt house in the St. Anthonie-breestraat in the centre of Amsterdam. He paid 13.000 Guilders in instalments. Many of his neighbours belonged to the Jewish community.

"The blind Fiddler"
signed and dated in monogram: *RHL 1631*

etching: 78 x 53 mm; complete with 1 mm margins

Bartsch 138; Seidlitz 138; Hind 38;
White-Boon 138, second state (of three)
Plate not in existence – with Nowell-Usticke (1967): R+
Condition: a very delicate 17th century impression,
with plate tone and good contrast

Provenance: with Boerner in 1856 Gustav F.K. Parthey, Berlin, 1798-1872 (Lugt 2014); from a private Dutch collection.

The interpretation that the fiddler could be blind, can perhaps be explained by the presence of a little dog walking just in front of him. The ease with which Rembrandt characterised the fiddler in his peculiar outfit, showing the refined outlines of his violin ready to play, enhance the amusing spirit of this intimate composition.

"The Hog" signed and dated: *Rembrandt f. 1643*

etching and drypoint: 145 x 184 mm;
with wide margins

Bartsch 157; Seidlitz 157; Hind 204;
White-Boon 157, first state (of two)
Plate not in existence –
with Nowell-Usticke (1967): C1+
Condition: an excellent, 17th century impression,
still with some burr

This is certainly a free-style etching, possibly inspired by
Rembrandt's visits to local farmers, perhaps even in the
company of his family. In 1643, his son Titus was two years
old and could well have been portrayed as the infant nearest
to the sow's head.

**"Portrait of Abraham Francen, Apothecary
and Art Collector"** circa 1657

etching, drypoint and burin: 158 x 208 mm;
with 2–3 mm margins

Bartsch 273; Seidlitz 273; Hind 291;
Wh.-B. 273, seventh-eighth state (of ten)
Plate in existence –
with Nowell-Usticke (1967): C2+
Condition: a fine 18th century impression with
good contrasts

The chemist/pharmacist Abraham Francen (born in 1613) was a close friend of Rembrandt's, and a guardian to Hendrickje
Stoffels and Rembrandt's daughter Cornelia (born in 1654). Apparently, he was an important art collector.
The changes from the sixth state onwards, altering the sitter's appearance, were possibly carried out by Watelet and later
Basan. It is also suggested that the early states portrayed Otto van Cattenburch, and that only in the sixth state did Rembrandt
transform the features into a likeness of Francen.

"Head of an Old Man in High Fur Cap" circa 1635

etching: 44 x 32 mm; complete with good margins

Bartsch 299; Seidlitz 299; Hind 135; **White-Boon 299, only state**
Plate not in existence – with Nowell-Usticke (1967): RRR-
Condition: a fine and delicate 17th century impression

Provenance: Karl Ferd. Friedrich von Nagler, Berlin (Lugt 2529); Kupferstich-
kabinett der Staatl. Museen, Berlin (Lugt 1632 and dupl. stamp Lugt 2398).

It is possible that, later, this little print has been reworked by a pupil. Nowell-Usticke and
Münz accept this print as 'entirely' by Rembrandt. Impressions are of the greatest rarity.

ALBRECHT DÜRER
(1471 - Nuremberg - 1528)

"Nemesis or The good Fortune"

signed with monogram in the plate,
and circa 1501-1502

engraving: 323 x 224; trimmed just
within the platemark; watermark: 'Hohe
Krone', Meder Watermarks no. 20 (used
between1480 - 1525); see for
comparison C.M. Briquet, vol. II, p. 296
no.4895: Arms of Leipzig 1498

Bartsch 77; Meder 72/II/b (of f);
Dodgson 33; Hollstein 72; Strauss 37

Provenance: on recto: old illegible
handwritten inscription in sepia ink;
on verso: with handwritten number
6370; from a private Dutch collection.

In one hand she holds a bridle with which she binds
man's pride, in the other a goblet containing riches
and honour to reward the just.

LUCAS VAN LEYDEN
(1494 - Leiden - 1533)

"Potiphar's wife accusing Joseph"
signed and dated *L 1512*

engraving: 123 x 161 mm; trimmed just
outside the borderline; Watermark:
Crowned shield with sun and pendant B
(Briquet 13798)

White-Boon 21 first state (of two);
Filedt Kok (1978) 21 a (of c)
Condition: A fine rich impression printed
with tone, of a quality now scarcely ever
encountered in the engravings

Provenance: Pierre Mariette, 1660
Albertina duplicate, sold Leipzig (C.G.
Boerner) auction 26, 1925, lot 799; Dr.
Albert W. Blum (Lugt 79b supplément)

EXPLANATORY NOTES ON REMBRANDT'S PRINT TECHNIQUE

The history of Engraving and Etching

As early as the 15th century, goldsmiths and engravers of weapons were the ones who possessed the expertise required for engraving. A first attempt at making an impression from an engraved metal would certainly have been done during this period. Even before 1450, engravings appear to have become independent artistic expressions. These products were mainly of German or Flemish origin.

At the end of the 15th century, it was Albrecht Dürer (1471-1528) who perfected the technique and enhanced the artistic value of engraving.

During the 16th century, the Italian Marcantonio Raimondi, and the Dutchman Lucas van Leyden followed him closely. Parallel to the graphic works of art, a flourishing trade developed in the form of printed 'playing cards'. Without a doubt, Lucas van Leyden (1494-1533) can be seen as the most important Dutch engraver, and his oeuvre of some 170 engravings has been of great influence on the development of Dutch printing.

In the middle of the 16th century, the focal point of all printing activities was still Antwerp. Plantijn played an important role in the book printing production, and Hieronymus Cock published large amounts of prints in his store. The Fall of Antwerp in 1585 stimulated the cultural development in the northern Provinces.

By the end of the 16th century, etching gained a place equal to engraving. Genres, and new trends such as realism, were stimulated through graphic techniques.

An important phenomenon was the difference between free etchers and the reproductive engravers. Painters discovered the etching technique as a means of free expression. This introduced the notion of 'painter-etcher'. The engraving was being relegated to the position of an excellent book illustration technique.

As the Northern Provinces liberated themselves from Spanish domination, a feeling of solidarity grew and the population enjoyed their newly gained independence. Their belief and strong willpower to make this independence last sent strong impulses to the economy and cultural life. The artistic beliefs connected to the decennia long European Mannerism was ready for renewal. There was an interest in daily life and reality in general. This, in turn, initiated a tendency towards realism. The sobriety proclaimed by the Protestant Church exerted additional influences on this development. Distribution made prints an excellent medium to propagate new ideologies and ideas.

Another important influence in Dutch art proved to be the German artist Adam Elsheimer (1578-1610), applying a renewed perspective in which the vanishing point was kept within the overall image. In addition, he made use of an exaggerated contrast between light and dark: the so-called "claire-obscure". He directly influenced the young Rembrandt.

The enormous graphic output of the 17th century can be divided into the following specialisations: landscapes, marines, portraiture, genre scenes, animal life, biblical subjects, italianates, and history.

Furthermore, the Bible has always played an important role in the lives of most artists. Rembrandt especially became an extraordinary exponent of impressive biblical prints. One of his popular Bible stories is the history of Tobit.

The origins of handmade Paper

Originally, a sheet of paper is a tissue of vegetable fibres, an Oriental invention that started in China in approximately 100 AD. They pounded and crushed stems of plants and leaves until they were left with a pasty substance of loose fibre. This so-called pulp, mixed with water, was evenly spread out over a mat and dried.
The Chinese tried to keep the papermaking process secret but it spread to Korea, which was then part of China and actively trading with Japan.

Between the 8th and the 11th centuries, the Persians and the Turks carried this process of papermaking from the Far to the Middle East. In Europe, the first traces can be found among the Moors in Spain in the 12th century, and at much the same time in southern Italy. France, southern Germany and Switzerland also had well-developed paper industries by the late 14th century. In England, white paper was first made in 1495, but on a large scale not until the 18th century.

The first paper mill in the southern Netherlands was established in Hoey as early as 1405. The northern Dutch Provinces only followed in 1586, with paper mills in Dordrecht and Alkmaar. Especially in the Netherlands during the 17th century, the use of paper increased enormously. Our own small production could not meet the demand, and much paper was imported from other European countries. On some occasions, those foreign mills were funded with Dutch money. A striking example is the popular watermark 'Weapon of Amsterdam', which nonetheless was printed in the production of French paper. It was not until the 18th century that the production of Dutch paper could meet the demand in Holland, and was even exported.

Most of the early Dutch paper mills - windmills - were located in the Zaanstreek, an area closely situated to the north of Amsterdam. Clean water and clean air was indispensable for clear fine paper.
Until 1800, European paper was made entirely of rags and hemp pulped in water by simple water-driven machinery. The demand for 'quality' rags grew to the point of scarcity. And by means of export bans for the rag trade, the authorities tried to support the national paper industry. Generally, rags were stripped of buttons, hooks, etcetera, and preferably needed to be white or of a light undyed colour. Subsequently, these rags were being pulverized in a specially constructed machine, called the *'hollander'*. Next, the crushed paper paste (pulp) was kept in barrels. Good quality drawing and etching paper was made in the traditional way by dipping a close-meshed wire mould into the pulp, and giving it a peculiar shake to consolidate the sheet.

The producer would often include his own watermark in the paper. He designed a crest made up of his monogram and a special emblem, and attached this to the meshed copper wire mould. Against the light, we are able to see the structure of the wiring of the mould and the thinner paper layer with the crest incorporated in it. For the most part, watermarks in handmade and old paper have been catalogued. Dating the paper of prints is highly important to determine whether the actual impression was made during the artist's lifetime.

To take the wet paper off the mould was an art in itself. The water would be lightly squeezed out, and the mould tipped over onto a sheet of felt. Then, the paper would be covered with another sheet of felt, and such a pile could grow to over a hundred sheets. The entire pile was called the 'post' and was sandwiched between two thick planks. After pressing out more water, the sheets were carefully taken off the felt, and piece by piece they were dried in a special drying-barn. The sheets were then pulled through a bucket with glue (gum) to close the small pores of paper. This method would improve its writability. Hot pressing, or the cheaper process of calendering between cylinders, was done to harden the sheets and smoothen their surfaces.

Finally, the handmade sheets of paper were cut to specific sizes and left the mill tied together in reams of 480 sheets at a time, ready for distribution to printers and publishers.

Less expensive etching and writing paper, and some book papers, were made of a mixture of cotton, hemp, esparto, and wood, with a good deal of china clay added to make them smooth and opaque.

Oriental papers, made of bamboo, rice straw and mulberry bark, would be imported for the artist's specific uses. Very thin sheets of Japanese mulberry paper are hand-glazed by rubbing them with stones. Engravers and etchers prefer these qualities for their proofs. Rembrandt, too, experimented with these different types of paper. He also used tinted - oatmeal - Japanese and Chinese paper, as well as vellum.

Papermaking machines, invented in France shortly before 1700, produced paper in rolls, but it was mainly sold cut to size.

Quality

In order to judge the quality of prints, it will be necessary to set some guidelines. For instance, what makes a fine Rembrandt print? Some collectors with small budgets would actually accept a printed impression from 1906, as long as it originated from the original plate. This would still make the impression a real Rembrandt.

If, however, the original plate has been reworked over the centuries, a good impression is much harder to achieve. It might show a heavier printed image, but the plate itself may have lost some of its original Rembrandt 'touch', although later impressions printed from the Basan album and after are still from the original plates. It is clear, though, that they can hardly compare to the beautiful early impressions from Rembrandt himself.

Especially in earlier impressions, the use of 'burr' is plainly visible. The freshly carved burin or drypoint grooves, where minute residues of copper stand up to either side of the drawn lines, cause burr. The ink on the plate will show these residues when the image is transferred onto paper. The more impressions are made and printing pressure of the plate continues, the flatter these upstanding residues will become, and the burr will soon disappear.

Several different states can be printed from an etching, because the artist or the printer wanted to make certain adjustments. This could vary from shaving off the sharp edges of the plate to getting rid of irregularities on the plate surface; to finishing off empty spaces like the sky in a landscape; or the addition of the artist's signature and, at a later stage, the invenit – fecit - excudit. If that same plate is handed down through time, deepening the grooves of the lines with a burin can make improvements of the quality.

Every collector will have to draw his own 'borderline of acceptance'. The various states of a period etching, printed on period paper under the supervision of the artist himself, are perfectly acceptable and legitimate. After the artist's death, however, we use the term 'late impression', and we should be more alert, because the print deteriorates from general 'wear and tear'. Paper and their watermarks help determine the right period.

Margins

The term 'margin' is used for the strips of paper sticking out over the plate edges. The presence of a visible paper margin secures the completeness of that print. Even a small margin is adequate proof. Especially in the 17th century, margins were cut to the plate edges to include these prints into larger albums.

Late Impressions

The later impressions have less value than the period prints from Rembrandt's time. It is important to know that after using the original plate, the artist or his publisher would scratch a large X in the surface of the subject matter to make the plate unusable. Only sporadically was the plate re-used for another image. To date, some eighty original Rembrandt plates have survived. Late in the 18th century, printing studios like Basan in Paris have reworked these plates. This diminished some of the originality of Rembrandt's own work. An extravagant example is the famous 'Hundred Guilder print'. In the early 1770's, the English Captain Baillie printed a few impressions, and decided soon after to rework the plate in order to achieve darker impressions. As a result, the image became somewhat inert and the head of Christ changed into a 19th century romanticist image. Baillie then cut the plate into five pieces, and made impressions of each of these smaller plates. In any case, the beautiful and complete impressions belong to the edition from approx. 1680, in fact, after Rembrandt's death. The watermark on the paper of this edition is a French Lilly in a large coat-of-arms.

Copies

During the course of the 17th century, printers and publishers applied for patents from the authorities. Such a patent could be granted for as long as 15 years. In this way, the trade in copies could be partly curbed.

Collector stamps and markings

These are markings put on the back/verso or even the front/recto of prints. They could be stamps, handwritten monograms, signatures, or other notes. The collector markings and notes tell us much about the provenance and the quality of prints.

Since 1921, many of these markings have been catalogued by the avid collector Frits Lugt in his "Les Marques de Collections", two volumes of which were published in 1956.

Classification

In 1967, the art historian G.W.Nowell-Usticke did an extensive study into the origins, the different states, and, most of all, the quality of Rembrandt's graphic oeuvre.

He has attempted to estimate the degree of rarity of Rembrandt's graphic oeuvre out of an estimated total of over 300 individual etchings, and printed during the 17th century only:

0	= unobtainable	(30 prints)
RRRR	= greatest rarity	(40 prints)
RRR	= extremely rare	
RR	= very rare / scarce	(50 prints)
R	= rare / very uncommon	(50 prints)
C1	= uncommon	(50 prints)
C2	= commonest	(50 prints)

Of his own accord, Usticke rejected circa 60 prints as not being by Rembrandt.

There is no certainty about the total number of impressions made of Rembrandt's prints. However, several experts have tried to make educated guesses about this popular question. In general, there may be an average of between 3 and 100 seventeenth century impressions of Usticke's 'R' classification (rarity); and between 100 and 300 seventeenth century impressions of his 'C' classification. We should of course be aware that these estimates concern all of the various states of each print. Of the early states, the number printed is relatively low. And not every print was published in the same volume.

Today, some of Nowell-Usticke C-classifications should be upgraded to R-classifications.

Restoration

Often a print has to be restored, preferably with a certified paper restorer. If the print has surface dirt, it can be easily cleaned using several specialised washing procedures. Small tears can be filled with paper; thin spots and margins can be strengthened. In some cases, it may be necessary to strengthen the complete back of the print with a thin layer of 'papier maché'. If a restoration is professionally and carefully executed and the damage remains 'within reason', such a procedure is perfectly acceptable.

Some criteria to watch for

First and foremost ... are you excited about the print?
If so, then you may wish to ask yourself the following:

Is it an authentic print, and not a copy or reproduction?
Is it printed on period paper from the artist's time?
What is the printed quality? If it requires 'burr' can you see enough of it?
Is there any damage, restoration, or cut within the plate mark?
In what state is the impression?
Is the price reasonable in comparison with similar prints?

"The more knowledge one possesses,
the more leniently one may judge"

"Beauty is in the eye of the beholder, which means
it exists in the consciousness of those who see it."

A BRIEF HISTORY OF REMBRANDT'S COPPERPLATES

In the spring of 1993, almost eighty of Rembrandt's original copper plates were sold on the London art market. The French print publisher Pierre-Francois Basan had put this collection together in the late 18th century, and it was now being individually sold from the estate of the American collector Robert Lee Humber. Humber himself had acquired the plates in 1938, and had never made much of an effort to publicize this addition to his collection. Only in 1956 were they exhibited at the North Carolina Museum of Art in Raleigh (USA). They had been locked away into the obscurity of a bank vault ever since Humber died in 1970.

As a result of various investigations to find out what had happened to Rembrandt's oeuvre of copperplates, it turned out, for example, that after Rembrandt's death at least 150 of his plates were in circulation, from which prints were still being made.

In the 17th century, there was a flourishing market in used copperplates. They passed from one publisher to another and were reprinted until demand for the subject matter was exhausted. Rembrandt generally used new, so-called 'cold-hammered' copperplates for his etchings. The fact that these plates were harder than the rolled plates of today, made it possible to obtain some 40-50 good impressions from each plate. Their thickness was usually 1 millimetre. The dry point gave a stronger and more durable burr. Rembrandt often made radical changes in a plate, and deleted passages by burnishing these scenes, some of which are still faintly visible. Sometimes, he cut off pieces to re-use them for another creation.

Rembrandt occasionally sold plates to his patrons, such as the one of 'Abraham casts out Hagar and Ishmael' (B.30), and the portrait of Jan Six (1618-1700; B.285). At the time of his bankruptcy, there is no mention of any Rembrandt etching plates. One of the reasons could be that they were exempted or 'technically' owned by his printers, which at least gave him the opportunity to keep using the tools of his trade and means of support, and still earn from their turnover and commission 'indirectly'. The best-known seventeenth century print dealer Clement de Jonghe (1624-1677) seemed to have owned many of the Rembrandt plates. In any event, a good number of his plates were in different hands after Rembrandt had died. It was customary for print dealers to add their address to them, especially after the artist's death. Posthumously, Claes Claesz. Visscher published his Rembrandt plates in the form of a booklet.

Even during the 17th and 18th centuries, connoisseurs knew the true value of fine impressions or rare and early states, meanwhile warning about copies and reworked plates. Also, collectors considered impressions on oriental paper highly desirable.

During the second half of the 18th century, the demand for Rembrandt prints was high. This resulted in many copies and imitations in the Rembrandt taste. In 1751, the growing demand led to the publication of the very first 'oeuvre catalogue' of Rembrandt etchings by the Parisian art dealer E.F.Gersaint (ca.1696-1750). One of the most praised characteristics of Rembrandt's etchings was the subtle way in which he managed to achieve such a high tonality. Later reprints hardly ever show such surface tone, for the simple reason that they had been reworked merely to repair the wear and tear of printing. The fact that Rembrandt had left various plates only half-finished was seen as a mystery. Some of these plates were finished during the 18th century by other engravers, using f.i. the mezzotint technique, as with the Amsterdam publisher Pierre Fouquet Jr. (1729-1800).

In 1775, Captain William Baillie restored the 'Hundred Guilder' plate with care and perception. He had acquired this plate from the Bostonian mezzotint engraver John Greenwood (1727-92), who had bought it in Holland shortly before. After printing some 100 impressions, Baillie cut up the plate in order to guarantee the exclusiveness of the original and complete print.

The whereabouts of the remaining Rembrandt plates during the 18th century remains a mystery. However, in the 1769 auction of Pieter de Haen's (1723-1766) estate, some 75 original Rembrandt plates turned up. In the 17th century, many of them had belonged to the print dealer Clement de Jonghe.

The Amsterdam art dealer Pierre Fouquet Jr. bought them. Shortly afterwards, they came into the possession of the Parisian writer, art critic and engraver Claude Watelet (1718-1786). He very much admired the chiaroscuro effects in Rembrandt's graphic oeuvre, and amassed a total of 83 Rembrandt plates.

In 1786, they were in turn bought by Pierre-François Basan (1723-1797), who had already gained an international reputation. His stock consisted of almost 5000 copperplates by old and modern masters. In 1789, he published a special 'receuil' devoted to Rembrandt, with an index list according to Gersaint's catalogue raisonné (Paris, 1744). A publication of this kind supports the more scientific approach to gaining historical knowledge not only of the actual work, but also of the artist himself and the period or school in which he was active. This meant that Basan's impressions have a different value, and merely became reproductions of the originals – original illustrations of the etchings of Rembrandt.

Later, in 1807 and 1809, his son Henry-Louis published this receuil again, but on rather inferior paper and of lower quality. In about 1810, the Parisian publisher Auguste Jean (who died in 1820) reworked the Basan plates, and in addition published a 'receuil', just as his widow did after 1820. Only after 1846, when the publisher and engraver Auguste Bernard acquired the plates from the estate of Jean's widow, were the impressions no longer sold in the familiar album format. Practically speaking, it was by now extremely difficult to obtain good impressions from the sometimes reworked plates.

In 1906, Rembrandt's commemorative year, L'Artiste (a French journal) attempted to plan a series of reprints from the by then faded and inferior plates. Luckily, this idea was abandoned. It would not have been good publicity for the late master Rembrandt himself.

Bernard eventually sold the almost 85 plates to Alvin-Beaumont. Apart from a small number of expensively printed portfolios of 'restrikes', and some individual impressions from the plates taken by the Canadian etcher Donald Shaw MacLaughlin (1876-1938), all of these existing plates were finally inked and varnished in 1916. They were placed in costly green leather mounts with their titles gilded, and in French, and set in ten large black frames.

Shortly before, a thorough investigation by the engraver A.C. Coppier (1867-1938) into their authenticity had revealed that many of the plates had actually survived almost untouched, different from the historic reputation by which we were led to believe that the plates had been heavily reworked during the centuries.

In 1921, the plates came to Amsterdam for an exhibition in the Palace of Industry. Afterwards, Alvin-Beaumont deposited them in the Rijksmuseum for seven years, but they were never purchased by the museum. In 1930, the plates were for sale and shown in New York. In 1937, the British Museum tried to negotiate a purchase, but at 600.000 French francs the asking price was too high.

It was not until 1938 that the collection of plates was sold for half that price to the American Robert Lee Humber, who placed them on loan in The North Carolina Museum of Art in Raleigh.

After Humber's death in 1970, the plates were kept in a bank vault until released for individual sale in 1993 through the London dealers Artemis. Since then, it has become clear that the plates were in good condition, and Rembrandt's original lines were well preserved.

Until well into the nineteenth century, the plates were regarded as a commodity by the various printers and publishers to meet the demand for Rembrandt's graphic work.

Today, the plates are generally valued as works of art in their own right.

"What you do
when you don't have to,
determines what you will be
when you can't help it...!"

Hello future... here we come...!

"A room filled with art, is a room of thoughts and emotions."

A SELECT AND ABBREVIATED BIBLIOGRAPHY

Ash, Nancy and Fletcher, Shelley, "Watermarks in Rembrandt's Prints", Washington 1998.

Bartsch, Adam, "Catalogue Raisonné de toutes les Estampes qui forment l'Oeuvre de Rembrandt, et ceux de ses principaux Imitateurs", Vienna, 1797, 2 vols.

Biörklund, G. with the assistance of O. Barnard, "Rembrandt's Etchings: True or False", Stockholm, London and Paris, 1955, revised edition 1968.

Briquet, C. M., "Les Filigranes", Leipzig 1923, 4 vols.

Heywood, Edward, "Watermarks, mainly of the Seventeenth and Eighteenth centuries", Hilversum, 1969.

Hind, Arthur M., "A Catalogue of Rembrandt's Etchings", London 1923, 2nd ed. 2 vols.

Hinterding, Erik, "The History of Rembrandt's Copperplates, with a catalogue of those that survive", Zwolle 1995 (trade edition of Simiolus, Netherlandish quarterly for the History of Art, vol. 22, 4, 1993-94).

Kornfeld, Eberhard and Stauffer, Christine, "120 Radierungen von Rembrandt der Jahre 1629 bis 1665", Auktion 170, 21 June 1979.

Laurentius, Theo, "Oude prenten, een handleiding voor verzamelaars", Lochem 1980.

Lugt, Frits, "Les Marques de Collections de Dessins et Estampes", Amsterdam 1921, Supplément Den Haag 1956.

Münz, Ludwig, "A Critical Catalogue of Rembrandts Etchings", London 1952, 2 vols.

Nowell-Usticke, G. W., "Rembrandt's Etchings, States and Values", New York 1988.

Ornstein van Slooten, Eva e.o., The Rembrandthouse: "The Prints, Drawings and Paintings", Amsterdam 1991.

Rovinski, Dmitri, "L'Oeuvre gravé de Rembrandt, Saint Petersbourg", text, 1 vol., plates, 3 vols 1890.

Seidlitz, Woldemar von, "Kritisches Verzeichnis der Radierungen Rembrandts", Leipzig 1895, 1922 revised.

White, Christopher, 'Rembrandt as an Etcher', London, 1969.

White-Boon, "Rembrandt van Rijn, Vol. XVIII and XIX, in: Hollstein's Dutch and Flemish Etchings, Engravings and Woodcuts", 2 vols, Amsterdam 1969.

A Collection of etchings by Rembrandt Harmensz.van Rijn (1606-1669), formed by Joseph R. Ritman, and presented for sale by Artemis and Sotheby's, 1995.

From December 10th 2005 until February 11th 2006, more than 50 Rembrandt etchings covering all aspects of his important oeuvre will be on display, about 35 prints of which will be for sale.
The exhibition will have a clear connection with the Rembrandt commemorative year in 2006.
In addition, there will be our own choice from "500 years of painting", both national and international.

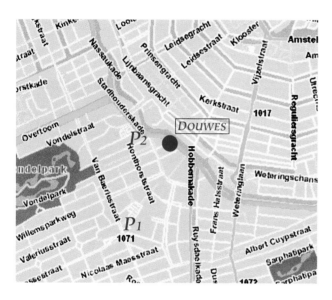

DOUWES FINE ART
Stadhouderskade 40
1071 ZD Amsterdam, The Netherlands
Tel. +31 (0)20 - 664 63 62 *Fax* +31 (0)20 - 664 01 54
E-MAIL: info@douwesfineart.com
INTERNET: WWW.douwesfineart.com

PARKING is only 4 minutes walk from the gallery:

P1: Museumplein
(entrance Van Baerlestraat, opposite the 'Concertgebouw')
or

P2: Byzantium
(next to the Vondelpark, access Stadhouderskade, entrance in the Tesselschadestraat)

Colofon

Publisher:	Douwes Fine Art, Amsterdam
Art direction:	Evert J.M. Douwes Jr.
Texts:	Evert J.M. Douwes Jr., and assistance.
English corrections:	Leen Don, Bunnik
Photography:	Evert J.M. Douwes Sr., Freek Esser (p. 20), Kees Kuil, Albert Roosenburg (p. 23, top).
Lithography:	Kees Kuil, Amsterdam
Design and production:	Kees Kuil, Amsterdam
Pre-press and printing:	Thieme Amsterdam
Binding:	Stokkink, Amsterdam

"Quality will show!"
The Jubilee-book on the occasion of 200 years *Douwes Fine Art* is printed
on **real art paper** *Zanders Mega,* 170 g/m², matt, delivered by *M-real Zanders* (since 1829).